UNWIND!

**Understand and
control life,
be better!!**

UNWIND!
Understand and control life, be better!!

DR DARREL O. HO-YEN
BMSc(Hons), MBChB, MRCPath, MD

DODONA BOOKS

First Published 1991
Reprinted: 1994

Copyright © Darrel O Ho-Yen,
1991

ISBN 0-951 1090-0-2-2

Publishers and distributors:
Dodona Books:
The Old Schoolhouse,
Kirkhill, Inverness,
IV5 7PE.

Designed and produced by
Words & Images, 2 Charlton
Cottages, Barden Road,
Speldhurst, Tunbridge Wells,
Kent TN3 0LH (0892) 862395.

Printed and bound in Great
Britain by Highland Printers,
Inverness.

CONTENTS

Stage two (Muscles). Stage three (Breathing). Stage four (Mind control): peaceful scenes, removing intruders, mantra. Stage five (Exit). Application. Summary.

Life. Stress. Obtain information: stop, look, listen. "IF". Identify problems: emotions, health, questions. Summary.

Use of time: your needs, your wants, priorities. Reward/effort ratio: the system, results, the future. Decision-making: solve problems (timescale, single question, more information, choices, decisions), good decisions (fear of being wrong, priorities, easy/difficult problems, no regrets). Summary.

Ill health: minor illness, serious illness, pre-existing illness. Reducing stress: behaviour, unwind, understand, control. Be better: self- improvement, happiness. Summary.

Demands of the environment: family and friends, job, finances. Personal resources: fears, strengths, weaknesses. Choosing: health, personal objectives, reduce demands, increase resources. Summary.

Skills. Disasters, submarine of life. Losing. Winning. Summary.

ABOUT THE AUTHOR

Dr Darrel Ho-Yen was born in Guyana, South America, but finished his schooling in London. After a year's Voluntary Service Overseas in the Caribbean, he went to medical school at Dundee University. He completed his training at the Regional Virus Laboratory, Ruchill Hospital, Glasgow. He is now Consultant Microbiologist at Raigmore Hospital, Inverness; Director of the Scottish Toxoplasma Reference Laboratory; and Honorary Clinical Senior Lecturer at Aberdeen University.

Dr Ho-Yen has had extensive experience in managing and counselling patients with Post Viral Fatigue Syndrome and wrote the first British book on this subject, **"Better Recovery from Viral Illnesses"**, in April 1985 (Second edition in 1987). He is also a co-author of the Oxford University Press textbook **"Diseases of Infection"** published in 1987 (second edition in preparation). Dr Ho-Yen has published numerous scientific papers and articles.

His experience on the needs of patients with chronic illnesses; the importance of being able to unwind, understand and control life has led him to write this book.

PREFACE

I see many patients whose lives are in a mess. This is not usually due to any reckless behaviour by the patients. More often, the patient's predicament was started by external factors such as infection or a major life event. Most patients were ill-prepared for these life disasters. Sadly, most patients were unable to relax or deal with the effects of stress.

Many books on the market deal with relaxation, or the effects of stress. However, almost all of my patients require one book that deals with both problems. In addition, patients were very wary of a technique that involved adopting a religion. This book is a result of the needs of patients. It is a result of my advice and counselling that has been given to the patients over many years. This advice has also been influenced by the patients themselves, and I would like to thank the many patients who have helped me to evolve the approach to life as explained in this book.

This book is aimed at the very many individuals with chronic illnesses. It is hoped that the information in this book will allow them to be more successful in dealing with life. First, individuals will need to develop relaxation skills. With these skills, they will then be able to learn to understand and control their lives. In time, and with much effort, their lives may slowly become better. Also, as I believe that prevention is always better than a cure, this book will allow those who are well to develop skills for the Game of living. If these skills are developed, individuals will be able to deal with life's disasters. More than this, these people could have a life of self-improvement and happiness.

Darrel Ho-Yen   1991

ACKNOWLEDGEMENTS

No book is published as a result of the efforts of one person. The idea for this book came from the many requests from patients and doctors for information on relaxation and management of stress. I am grateful to these individuals for prompting me to write this book. I am also grateful for the understanding of Jen, Gregory and Colan during the writing of this book. I would like to thank Mr Alan McGinley who was exceptionally helpful in the preparation of the front cover. I would also like to thank Diane Drummond of Words & Images for her patience and professional approach to the preparation of this book. Jean Chatterton, Roger Evans and David Ashburn were good enough to read the many proofs of this book and offer constructive comments. Lastly, I am indebted to Miss Vivian MacFarquhar for her patience, resilience and expertise through the many drafts of this book.

CHAPTER ONE
INTRODUCTION

Many people have great difficulties with their lives. These difficulties are a result of the stress of modern life. **The demands being made by society on individuals can produce ill health**. Unfortunately, most people do not recognize the cause of their ill health. Instead, they visit their doctors with a variety of complaints. Predictably, doctors can do little to alleviate such complaints, and many patients end up turning to alternative medicine.

There is no doubt that living in a modern, jet-age society produces great demands on individuals. Somehow, ordinary people are expected to be able to cope with these demands. When people fail, there is little outside help; but worse, matters usually deteriorate further. However, because of the media especially television, **most people regard failure as a reflection of themselves.** Therefore, they try and ignore failure, push themselves harder and hope to get out of their predicament. It is a forlorn hope and many people are destined for greater failure. The truth is that **many individuals have not been given the opportunity to acquire the skills to survive in a modern society**.

The object of this book is to explain the skills necessary for survival in a modern society. The most important skill is the ability to unwind. Detailed instruction on how this may be achieved is in Chapter Five: Plan to unwind. **It will take time before the skill to unwind can be developed**. Fortunately, most people, with commitment and energy, will be able to perfect the skill. It is well worth persisting even if you find it difficult as the rewards are great.

The greatest reward of being able to unwind is the benefit from the fourth stage (mind control) of the Plan to unwind. This stage allows you to obtain information on your life. **You will be able to identify problems in your life**. This is especially important in the areas of stress in your life as most people are unable to recognize such problems. With this information you will develop an understanding of life (Chapter Six). However, such knowledge needs to be taken further before you are able to control life (Chapter Seven). This chapter will highlight the importance of the use of time, the reward/effort ratio and good decision-making. **If these skills can be mastered, you will be able to control your life**.

The real benefits from using the techniques in this book is that you will be able to be better. For many, the benefits in better health would be the most welcome. The good news is that these benefits are only the start. As one becomes more adept at unwinding and mind control there are other, greater prizes. Fortunately, such prizes can be achieved by everyone. **Most readers will become better by self-improvement and**

greater happiness (Chapter Eight).

This book allows you to see your life objectively. You will be able to see the demands being made on you by your family, your friends, your job and your financial situation. These demands are being balanced by your own personal resources (your fears, your weaknesses and your strengths). Your life is the result of this balance. However, with the skills emphasized in this book, **you will be able to reduce the demands being made on you and increase your own personal resources**. The path will not be easy. Acquisition of all skills require considerable time, effort and commitment. For many, it will take many months; for others, it will take many years. **It is most difficult to start**. If you can start to learn, it will be a journey that you will enjoy.

This book was written for several reasons. The major objective was to highlight ways in which it can be easier to cope with the demands of society. The attitudes in this book are a result of techniques that have been used successfully on many individuals. **These techniques have also been chosen because they can work for you**. In the Game of living (Chapter Ten), there are many winners and losers. However, the important factors are the development of skills and the ability to deal with disasters.

This book is also about choosing. The freedom to choose is often taken for granted. Yet, choosing is a precious gift. It is hoped that this book will provide you with information on yourself. With this information, it will become obvious how you are coping with life. **You will be able to choose what you want out of life**. More importantly, you will recognize that there is a need to develop skills in the Game of living. With the development of such skills, you have the opportunity for self-improvement, happiness and to be better.

SUMMARY

1. The demands being made of individuals by society can produce ill health. Most people regard failure as a reflection of themselves. However, many individuals have not been given the opportunity to acquire the skills to survive in a modern society.

2. This book allows you to see your life objectively. You will be able to reduce the demands being made on you and increase your own personal resources.

3. The skills advocated in this book have been used successfully by many individuals. These skills may work for you, but require your time and effort.

4. The greatest benefit of these skills is that you have the opportunity to choose what you want out of life.

CHAPTER TWO
WHY UNWIND?

Andy, a young man who had moved from the country to the town, was keen to find a suitable church. He valued the sermon most, and so he methodically visited all the churches to listen to the various preachers. He even went to the children's talk. One day, he heard a minister tell the story of how oysters cope with life's irritations. With great feeling, the minister produced a pearl and asked the children to pass it around. Whilst this happened, he explained how the oyster had got a piece of gravel inside him, but dealt with the irritation by covering it with many coats of smooth material. In the end, there was no irritation but something beautiful which all could admire. He finished by asking Jimmy who was holding the pearl:

"Jimmy, was not the oyster clever?"

"No." replied Jimmy with great conviction. "Why not?" asked the minister with obvious disbelief.

"Because people have killed him to get the pearl!"

This story made Andy laugh, and although he was impressed with Jimmy, he was not on the same wavelength as the minister. Andy's search finally came to an end at an evening service. He was late and was able to only hear the end of the sermon: "We have not done those things which we should have done. Instead, we have done those things which we should not have done."

Andy quickly sat down with relief and whispered:

"Thank heavens, I've found my lot!"

This book is for the Andys of the world. **It is for people who are doing things that they should not be doing**. Most of these individuals are not aware of the consequences of their actions even though the results may be unhappiness or ill health.

WHY UNWIND?

For many people, this question is very reasonable. They would say that to do well in the modern world, a person needs to be "keyed up" and "ready to go". Someone who has unwound would never get anything done and was best described as a "wimp". Superficially, these comments appear sensible. Life is about living; living is about movement. However it is wrong to be only wound up, as it is wrong to be only unwound. Living a full life involves movement between these two states; **a person needs to be wound up at certain times and unwound at others**. Whilst most people are able to wind themselves up, only a minority are able to unwind. Individuals who are able to choose their mental state (wound up or unwound) have greater control of life. This control allows better decisions to be made.

Why have I chosen to use the word **"unwind"** instead of **"relaxation"**? Both of these words have similar meanings, however, there are important differences. Firstly, relaxation is usually more associated with muscles, for example "make less rigid", whereas this book is more concerned with the relaxation of the mind. Secondly, relaxation is often associated with "recreation". Although the concept of re-creating (or "making again") is consistent with this book, other interpretations of recreation (such as "interval of free time") are not the objectives of this book. Lastly, "unwind" epitomizes this book with its approach of "undoing", "unravelling" or "disentangling" life's problems.

When a person learns to be a spectator, there is the potential for a greater understanding of relationships (with family and friends) and situations (jobs and finances). A greater understanding also allows greater control of life. This control is best defined as offering more choice in life. **Thus, the sequence of events is: unwind and understand your life; with this knowledge, you will have the potential to control life, and be a better person.**

Understand life

Many individuals are so busy living that there is no time for reflection. Activities occupy every waking hour. Questions, such as "Why am I doing this?", "What do I want from life?", "Where am I going?", or "Am I happy?" are never asked. Sometimes it requires a major disaster, for example the death of a parent to stop people from their frenetic activity. Many individuals are under stress. Of the many different definitions of stress, I like:

Stress is a process in which the resources of the person are matched against the demands of the environment.

The demands of the environment are made up of those around you (family and friends) and situations that you are in (job and finances). The family is the most important and so should require the most time and effort. Instead, the majority of the population expend most of their energies on their job. There are many good reasons why a job is important, however it is usually the means to an end. If the quantity of time and effort which is spent on the family is small, it is critical that it should then be of the highest quality. **It is very easy to take the family for granted**.

In the first quarter of life, friends may appear to be the reason for living. This is a stage in life. With maturity, the nature of friendship changes and becomes subordinate to the family. Similarly, early in life, money can be a major objective in life. Again, with maturity one recognizes that money is only a tool with which one obtains the major objectives in life. Thus, money does not by itself bring happiness, but allows people to have time which they may spend on activities which bring happiness. As Bacon said: **"Money is a good servant but a bad master."**

Control life

Many people often consider individuals who control life to be the opposite of those that are "spontaneous". As spontaneity is deemed to be a desirable characteristic, control of life is frequently avoided. The argument is similar to that with being wound up/unwound. However control of life allows individuals to exercise choice; they can choose to be spontaneous. Sadly, the business of living is actually a matter of organisation. If you want **to have time to be spontaneous, you have to be organised**. Individuals who are not organised have less time to be spontaneous than those who are organised. However, even with the best organised, the unpredictability of life ensures that perhaps only about three-quarters can be controlled. There are **three skills to control life: use of time, the reward/effort ratio and decision-making**.

The **use of time** is so simple that it is frequently overlooked. For some unknown reason, everyone feels that they are using time to its fullest. There is often the plaintive cry "I'm doing the best I can" or "I was up all night". These are just excuses, and would not be uttered if the individual could say "Here is the assignment a week ahead of the deadline!" or "This is the best work I have ever done!". To understand if you use time well, you need to recognise what others could achieve in the same time. Of course, the immediate answer is that those who achieve more are more clever. In reality, those who achieve more are usually not more clever but better organised. They

21

use time well. They tend to spend time doing what they **want** to do, instead of what they **have** to do.

One great secret in the control of life is the **reward/effort ratio**. This requires that each solution to a problem should be assessed. **The best solutions are those where there is maximum reward for the minimum effort**. Thus, a solution which gives 100 units of reward for 10 units of effort is probably a lot better than a solution which offers 200 units of reward for 400 units of effort. Yet, most individuals like to go for the "tops" or "the big one". The fact that someone else in the same line could achieve 4000 units of reward with different projects is quickly explained as "luck", "contacts" or "those who have, always get more".

To be able to control life, **decision-making** is essential. It is believed by many that the ability to make decisions is something one is born with. This is not correct. Like much of life, decision-making can be learnt. There are five stages: identify the problem, obtain information, assess priorities, establish choices and make a decision. You must also always try to tackle the most difficult problem first. It does not matter if you do not succeed, but you must at least try. Often, whilst you are trying to solve the difficult problem, the easy problems disappear. You need to choose the best solution for yourself. The best solution may not be the best solution for anyone else. **Decisions are personal, and they should be so as you will be the person who has to live with the decision**. Nevertheless, you should always try to make a decision which is a true reflection of yourself.

Be better

If you can unwind, understand and control life, you will be better in many ways. In particular, there will be more happiness, better health and wealth. Although this seems to be a lot, these end results require some explanation. The process of being able to unwind allows you to see your life differently. Thus, your perception of happiness, health and wealth at the start will not be the same as after you are able to unwind. Happiness is very subjective. **The potential for happiness is perhaps the only thing that is equal in the world**. It does not depend on circumstances, money or ability. However, if you do not want to be happy, nothing can make you happy. Whilst if you want to be happy, every day you can be.

There is a preoccupation with **health** in the modern world. **For many, health has become the same as youth**. Thus, these individuals try to look younger, and expect their bodies to be able to do the physical acrobatics of youth. These attitudes are unrealistic, as growing old is part of living. Maturity involves a recognition that there are stages in life and each stage has advantages and disadvantages. Much energy and activity of youth is both wasteful and unproductive. To have good health at 45 years of age does not mean you could run a marathon, but rather that **you are in a state of well-being, both mentally and physically**. Indeed if you felt that you had to run marathons at age 45 years, one may want to ask a few questions about your mental health.

It is often easy to confuse money with wealth. A good definition of **wealth is a state of well-being that you appreciate**. There are two important points about this definition. The first is that it is also a possible definition of health, and indeed perhaps good health is the greatest wealth. The second point is that the individual needs to appreciate his/her position. Often one person's position may be regarded as wealth, whereas the person feels impoverished. For most people, wealth is well-being associated with money or possessions. Although this is reasonable, one should remember that money and possessions are only a small part of well-being.

SUMMARY

1. "Unwind" is probably a better word than "relax" as it emphasizes mental as compared to physical relaxation. Its synonyms ("undoing", "unravelling" or "disentangling") also conjure the right mental images for this book.

2. The sequence of events envisaged in this book is: unwind and understand your life; with this knowledge, you will have the potential to control life, and be a better person.

3. Stress is a process in which the resources of the person are matched against the demands of the environment. Almost everyone is under some stress. You need to understand the demands of the people (family and friends) and situations (job and finances) around you.

4. The three skills to control life are: the use of time, the reward/effort ratio and decision-making. You should use time to do what you **want** to do and not what you **have** to do. The best solutions involve the least effort. Decision-making involves the following process: identify the problem, obtain information, assess priorities, establish choices and make a decision.

5. The rewards of this approach to life is that you will be a better person. You could be happier, healthier and wealthier; however the way these words are used in this book is not what many people might expect.

CHAPTER THREE
THE PROBLEM

Children learn from their parents. Sometimes, it can be quite frightening to see how much they do learn. When both parents are working, the children's perception of their parents may be quite revealing. There is the story of the girl who was starting primary school. On the first day, the teacher asked the class: "How many seasons are there in the year?" The girl's hand was first to be raised, and she replied:

"Three. Holidays, busy season and very busy season."

Many adults have lost an appreciation of the seasons. Their lives are full of activities and there is just not enough time in each day. For their children, this can be seen to be more real than the outward changes in the climate brought about by the seasons of the year. This is sad. **In the modern world, many people are so busy living that they have little time to appreciate the world around them.** Today, more than ever, most people have great potential to control their lives. Yet, many of us behave as twigs in a whirlpool – taken around and around, and having no choice until they are thrown out onto the land. Yet, it is possible to behave differently. There can be great control of lives, but first you have to learn that **what you are is not what society makes you. What you are is what you have made yourselves**.

PEOPLE'S ATTITUDES

Mary is a housewife with two children, aged four and seven years. She gets up early to make breakfast for her husband, Mike. He works long hours, but earns a good salary and likes the house to look neat and tidy. Mary drops the older child to school and then takes the youngest child to playgroup. She is quite proud that she organises the playgroup, and is willing to spend her mornings making sure that everything runs well. Her afternoons are taken up with shopping, housework, gardening, decorating and looking after the family's pets. Her eldest child has activities three nights a week and she is glad that he is learning so much. She goes to keep-fit classes once a week and usually ends up baby-sitting on another night. She feels tired a lot and compensates by eating chocolates. Lately, she has not felt totally fulfilled and so she has enrolled for an Open University course. She feels that this would make her a better person, a more understanding mother and an interesting wife.

Brian was thrilled to be accepted to do Physics at college. He had done languages at school, but after a holiday job in the local hospital, he decided to change to science. He worked hard and deserved to be at college. At first, all was well. He had a great time. There were so many societies, dances, activities and opportunities for long discussions late into the night. However, within a few weeks he knew that he was out of his depth. He could not cope with the mathematics and his limited background knowledge did not help. Matters were desperate, but the examinations were not for another two months. Then he recalled that his favourite teacher once said, "A fit mind in a fit body". That was the answer. He started playing rugby again. Fortunately, he was good and popular. Everyone wanted to know him. It was wonderful. He spent most nights in the bar, but then, he could not disappoint his friends.

Karen was proud that she was a successful accountant in a man's world. She worked twice as hard as her contemporaries, and was an expert in power dressing and in the witty, sarcastic remark. Her single-mindedness had brought her success. Although she had no real friends, in business friends can be a handicap and prevent you from making difficult decisions. Her parents were impressed at her achievements, but wanted grandchildren. They also felt that she drank too much. She had an answer; she usually had an answer for everything. In her job, entertainment was part of the job, and it was important to be able to drink but still make the right decisions. Indeed, men often tried to ply her with drinks. Karen was proud that she could outdrink most men that she knew. Nevertheless, lately she had not found as much pleasure in her job. She was beginning to think of other things in her life. At first, Karen did not understand what was happening, but she interpreted this as a sign of weakness and her getting older. Her answer was to work harder and attempt the tasks that others felt were impossible. She would show the world. Although this meant more work and she drank more, it would be worth it. After all, nothing is achieved without sacrifice.

Fred was looking forward to his retirement, but had not anticipated the death of his wife. He had always organised all of his affairs, and kept his wife on the straight and narrow. Suddenly he was lonely with lots of time. Fred's philosophy was "For Satan finds some mischief still for idle hands to do", so he always kept active. Recently he had started to develop muscle and joint pains. The pain was so bad that he could not sleep. He started taking paracetamol regularly but obtained only short periods of pain relief. His doctor advised him to relax as he seemed anxious. Fred's reaction was that he was sitting in front of the television most of the day and so could not relax any more. He had worked all his life and usually most weekends and now he was watching television; it was obvious that previously he had been active and now he was relaxing. His young doctor observed that Fred appeared tense with fists clenched and could not sit still. At this point, Fred had had enough. He jumped up and stormed out of the surgery with derogatory comments about "smart", young doctors.

These four case histories have many common features. All were of individuals who had achieved a lot out of life, in the way that achievements are usually measured by our society. **All had equated activity with success, although activity can be unproductive and results are better equated with success**. In all cases, their approach to life had produced problems, yet their solution was to pack in more of the same. The results were that the problems became bigger, but they could not see this. They had gone down a road that led to a bog and the car had got dirty. Their solution was to reverse, stop and go down the same road twice as fast, with the certain belief that somehow the bog would disappear and the car would become clean. It is a peculiar logic.

These individual's approach to difficulties is to try and overcome the difficulty with more activity.

Can adults learn from children? The answer is usually no. The reason is that many adults see their role as teaching children. Yet, many characteristics of children such as open-mindedness and honesty are very commendable. The Bible advocates some of a child's attitudes: "unless you can change and become like little children you will never enter the Kingdom of heaven" (Matthew, 18.3). However, many adults would not be able to understand this. The difficulty is that adults feel that they know the answers, especially as they were once children.

The truth is that children can teach adults much in terms of relaxation. Adults often marvel at the ease with which a child sleeps: wherever it wants, whenever it wants. The child does not need an alarm clock to wake, but instead, a child wakes when the time is right (often wrong for the adult). Children, like animals, enjoy awakening. They stretch, they yawn. They open their eyes, they close their eyes and then they smile. Adults often pride themselves on being able to dress and be in the bathroom in under a minute.

LIFE EVENTS

Whilst some adults create their own problems; for others,

problems result from life events that are imposed on them. Certain events, such as war or a nuclear reactor accident can be appreciated by everyone as being sufficiently severe to change the lives of men, women and children. Paradoxically, as these events usually affect large numbers of people, their consequences are more easily identified. It is far more difficult to identify an individual's response to the vagaries of life. There have been several attempts to list the events that may occur in an individual's life in terms of their effects on that individual. Death of a spouse is the most severe, followed by divorce and marital separation. Understandably, these unhappy events have profound effects on the participants.

Happy events, such as marriage, holidays or the birth of a child, can equally affect the individuals concerned. In reality, **many things that people do can have an effect on them, often without their being aware of its importance**. In some cases, these events are uncontrollable, such as death or accidents; in other cases, events may be brought about by the individual, such as buying a new house or a car. These events may be one-off, for example a child leaving home, a spouse starting or finishing work. Alternatively, these events may be continuous, for example the way people drive their cars or how they interact socially with those around them. **The ways that individuals react to their life events are a reflection of their ability to deal with the world**. Simply, the way people live affects the way they feel; the things they do influences what they are.

1. Death

Death is a part of living, and is always accompanied by emotion. Feelings of regret, anger, guilt, frustration, sadness and appreciation are all very common. When someone has had a long illness, death may be regarded as a release and a blessing. **Where death is sudden, there is usually a feeling of missed opportunities**, often much had not been said. It is noteworthy that the death of a spouse is a third more severe than the death of a close family member, and two and a half times more severe than the death of a close friend. Marriage is one's biggest emotional investment and its end must have far-reaching results. With all death, there is a period of mourning which may extend to 6-12 months. During this time, there are several recognized stages: initially, there is disbelief; with automatic behaviour followed by depression, often with the feeling that the dead person is near; then, the relationship with the dead person is reviewed, accompanied by blame for the death and appreciation of the individual; and finally, there is a gradual recovery. **The effects of death on the survivor depend on the relationship with the dead person and the character of the survivor**. Although death is final and should not be surprising, its effects are profound. Often, this is because those alive expected the dead person to live longer, and consequently they did not express their true feelings to the individual before death.

2. Relationships

To live in a community, it is almost impossible not to interact with those around you. On one level, such social interaction constitutes personal relationships, however, to be meaningful individuals have to become involved with someone else. Involvement with one another keeps communities together. These relationships take time and effort to establish and grow. Unfortunately, in the modern, instant world, many expect too much too quickly. Further, advertisements in the media emphasize that with a particular product, the world would quickly fall in love with you. As the high divorce rate testifies: **people expect too much and are not prepared to work at relationships**. The stark truth is that a meaningful relationship is not a right of every individual. Instead, it is something that needs a lot of effort and luck. Those who have wonderful relationships are the lucky ones; they are not the majority.

For love, many would be happy to try hard, but this in itself is a handicap. In 1966, C.S. Lewis said "Many things – such as loving, going to sleep or behaving unaffectedly – are done worse when we try hardest to do them." Many who try very hard are doomed to failure. For success, one needs to be oneself, content and appreciate the richness of what one already has. **This involves a proper appreciation of commitment, both to one's family and friends**. There must also be a realisation that sometimes people grow apart. When this happens it is best to part with little recrimination, and try to preserve the good aspects of the relationship as treasured memories.

3. Finances

In the past, people usually bought what they could afford. Today, with inflation, the opposite is the norm. It makes some sense to buy on credit as you get the object of your desires immediately, and pay back with money that is worth less as it becomes inflated. However, the logic of this position depends on inflation being greater than the interest rate. Sadly, this is rarely the case and yet many individuals do not recognize that they are paying more for their purchases. The second problem of buying on credit is that many people do not recognize how much they owe. Thus, they frequently commit themselves to paying back an unrealistic proportion of their earnings. **Financial problems are common and their avoidance requires an understanding of money.**

The great problem about debt is that the solution usually involves repayment, bankruptcy or death. Understandably, repayment is the usual option, but it is also a **contract on time**. When one contracts to repay money over several years, one is making decisions on one's future. Thus, there is the need to keep on working to service the debt, and there is the necessity to avoid further commitments. These are quite severe restrictions on an individual's freedom. It is said that financial problems are responsible for most damage to relationships.

4. Work

Why do we work? Perhaps, George Elliot was correct when he said: "There's many a one who would be idle if hunger didn't pinch him; but the stomach sets us to work".

Many work to eat and the individual who would work for the joy of the work is rare. Nevertheless, work does have several other surprising benefits. Thus, with a good day's work, there is a feeling of accomplishment, self-esteem, self-worth and a greater enjoyment of recreation. These benefits are closely related to the work and can disappear with unemployment. Thus unemployment is a stressful situation.

As most of our lives is spent at work, it is not unexpected that there are other psychological factors. Work is also a reflection of an individual's ambition, success, satisfaction and attitude to life. Consequently, there are many who are extremely stressed at work. This stress can be overwhelming, especially as so much time is spent at work. **Individuals who can see work as part of life, rather than the reason for living have a great insight.**

5. Illness

Illness is often totally disruptive to oneself and one's family. Fortunately, illness is usually short, and everyone can breathe with relief when it is all over. The feelings of helplessness, anxiety and sometimes anger are quickly forgotten. Many people even take great pride in being "terrible patients". **Somehow, it is deemed to be a great sin if one is a good patient**, as if one is a good patient one is probably enjoying being ill. It is all totally illogical. However, as many people think in this way, it is somehow accepted as true.

As most of the population are not good at dealing with short illnesses, it is not surprising that the position with long illnesses is a total disaster. Unfortunately, the option of ignoring the individual's own shortcomings is no longer available. Instead, the person who is a "terrible" patient is eventually totally isolated. As the years pass, patients need to be able to change many of their attitudes. If this can be done, the chances of happiness and perhaps even recovery are increased. **The sadness is that many patients are unable to change, even though there is probably ample evidence that their approach is making them unhappy and isolated.** It seems that, as adults, many are unable to learn. Many are unable, or unwilling, to look at how they have spent their months or years of illness. If they are able to look at themselves as others see them, they may realise that they are their own worst enemies.

SUMMARY

1. In the modern world, many people are so busy living that they have little time to appreciate the world around them.

2. The major problem is people's attitudes. Activity can be equated with success, although activity can be unproductive and results are better equated with success. When such individuals have difficulties, they try to overcome the difficulty with more activity.

3. Many adults may benefit from approaching life with some of the attitudes of children such as open-mindedness and honesty.

4. Whilst some adults create their own problems; for others, problems result from life events that are imposed on them. The way that individuals react to these life events are a reflection of their ability to deal with the world.

5. Death of a spouse or a close friend is difficult to deal with and is complicated by a period of mourning. The effects of death on the survivor depend on the relationship with the dead person and the character of the survivor.

6. Good relationships are not a right of an individual.

7. Financial problems are common and their avoidance requires an understanding of money.

8. Work and unemployment are stressful to many people. Work must be regarded as part of life rather than the reason for living.

9. Many people are unable to deal with illness. When illness lasts for years, individuals need to change their life styles.

CHAPTER FOUR
HISTORY OF UNWINDING

There is a great temptation for people to think that life now is full of modern discoveries. Those who lived many years ago just could not have had all of the knowledge and opportunity that is available today. Although in many ways this is true, it is also true that much remains the same.

Fred enjoyed reading the newspapers. He had done so, every day, for 50 years. His wife always marvelled that he got so much pleasure out of reading the newspapers. One day she heard him chuckling and said:

"What is new in the papers today?"

"Nothing much." Fred replied.

"What do you find so amusing then?" his wife asked.

"Well," said Fred, "There is nothing new in the papers today.

It is just the same things happening to different people!"

In this chapter, some of the historical attitudes to unwinding will be considered. Most of the older methods are from the East and are often part of religious beliefs. The newer, Western methods are usually not related to religious beliefs but are skills to be developed, not unlike being skilful at a sport. With the Eastern attitudes there is an emphasis on being passive; whereas with the Western attitudes there is an emphasis on being active.

There is a great advantage in not having an unwinding technique as part of a religion as an individual may like the technique but not the religion. With many techniques, a teacher is required. In the West, such teachers may make extravagant claims to justify their large fees. Apart from large fees, these "teachers" often blame the failure of the student on the student's own inadequacy. In the end, it can be easier to embrace a religious belief rather than learn from an expensive "teacher". As always, the success of the pupil depends on the professionalism of the teacher.

EASTERN ATTITUDES

Eastern civilisations have a rich history in which the process of being able to unwind is part of religious belief. In many religions such processes are described as meditation ("to think about something deeply", "to reflect deeply on spiritual matters"). Important doctrines which have influenced the development of the approach in this book are briefly discussed.

1. Buddhism

Siddharta Gautama was born on the border between India and Nepal. He was later called "Buddha" (the enlightened one). Although he lived in a religious world of Hinduism, Buddha had very different beliefs, and for example abandoned the caste system and did not believe in the existence of a god. Buddha felt that individuals should have insight and awareness of their lives. With this knowledge, each person may become enlightened. He saw the objective of life as "nirvana" which means "extinction"; this is not an extinction of the self which would be a Buddhist heresy. **Instead, it is an extinction of the person's continuous need to do, to get, to achieve and to have material things.**

2. Taoism

This great Chinese religion was quite different from Confucianism. Whereas Confucianism seeks to make men and women perfect within the world, Taoism is about living in peace with oneself and one's environment. It has a great deal in common with the many "Green" movements in the West today. Taoism was perhaps a necessary contrast to Confucianism. Confucius was interested in rules of society and to become wise. The Taoists were more **concerned with doing nothing, being natural and searching for immortality.**

Not surprisingly, someone (Lin Chao-en) tried to combine the best features of the three great religions of his time. There was the Taoist's environmental sense, the Buddhist meditation and Confucian preoccupation with order in society. These three main influences probably still permeate Chinese society.

3. Zen

Zen originated from China under the name of Ch'an, the chinese for meditation. In China, there was much opposition to Ch'an and it was its arrival in Japan that saw its growth. Japanese Zen involves the practice of meditation under strict rules. The Samurai adopted the teaching as a means of self-discipline. In some ways, **Zen combines the "do nothing" of the Taoists and the "insight and awareness" of the Buddhists**. The "koan" (riddle) is of great importance and has the objective of exhausting the brain. A famous koan is "You know the sound of two hands clapping, what is the sound of one hand clapping?" The student may be asked to meditate on this all day and to give the master the answer at night. The master is usually never satisfied irrespective of the answer given. After many days (or weeks), a bizarre answer, such as blowing a raspberry, is greeted with ecstasy by the master. The reason is that the student has temporarily freed himself from his logical, thinking process.

4. Yoga

Yoga originates from India and Hinduism. The word means

"union" or "method". The object is **to unite the body, mind and emotions for a harmonious life**. In one teaching it is only the activity of the mind which keeps individuals from an awareness of their true selves. Thus, yoga is a method with which the mind can be controlled, so that an individual's true self becomes apparent. There are four classical forms of yoga. Self-realisation is obtained through purification of the body (hatha); repetition of a sacred word (mantra); control of the mind (raja); and absorption of the mind in inner sounds and lights (laya). Yoga can also be classified in relation to different approaches to God. In the West, the most common form is hatha which means "force". The object is that an individual achieves self-realisation through great effort with the help of certain postures (asanas) and breath control (pranayama). There are seven stages of hatha yoga: the first four are concerned with the body, and the last three with the mind.

In the West, yoga has been regarded as a way of strengthening the body and providing relaxation and a quiet mind. Thus, much of a person's stress and anxiety can be reduced. These are really quite limited objectives; and perhaps it should be remembered that in the context of Hinduism, yoga is a means to salvation.

WESTERN ATTITUDES

As in the East, Western attitudes to unwinding were part of religious beliefs. However, this century has seen dramatic changes in people's attitudes in the West. Firstly, there has been great **emphasis on an individual's right to choose**. The result is that many people are unwilling to accept an entire package, such as a religion; but, would want to choose the bit that they want, such as meditation. The obvious disadvantage of this attitude is that the commitment is superficial, and often the greatest benefit of any bit depends on the other parts of the whole.

The second factor that has influenced attitudes is the growth of the sciences. There is a feeling that anything good must have a scientific basis and must be easily explained. Of course, such attitudes are naive. In reality, **science despite its tremendous advances is at an early stage of development**. It is probably still true to say that all scientific knowledge is but a grain of sand on the beach of total knowledge.

1. Christianity

Christianity is descended from the religion of the Jews and is based on the teachings and life of Jesus Christ. There are many varieties of Christianity and many of the attitudes of older religions are present in Christianity. Through prayer it is possible to know God, and the **Christian aims to be united with God through Jesus Christ**. Christian prayer may emphasize the performance of good deeds and the avoidance of sin. This active position in the community is taken a stage further with the "Liberation Theology" movements of the developing countries. These seek to involve God in current social and political problems.

Another approach to Christian prayer is one that

concentrates on knowing God and his attributes. "Do you not know that you are God's temple and that God's Spirit dwells in you?" (I Corinthians, 3. 16). Thus, **individuals should seek the path to God within themselves**. This approach is emphasized by the "born again" Christians who see Christians as individuals opening themselves to the grace of God.

2. Psychotherapy

Psychotherapy is a process by which a therapist tries to uncover some of the influences of a patient's abnormal behaviour. In its most intensive form, psychotherapy involves spending a lot of time over a long period with a highly trained practitioner. In a simpler form, individuals identify sources of anxiety and stress by single or group counselling. Many believe that counselling and psychotherapy have replaced the church's confessional. Thus, the confessor listens to the penitent and absolves sins through the grace of God. Whilst the therapist listens to the patient and attempts to transform neurosis into acceptable behaviour.

In some communities, especially in the United States, nearly everyone has a psychotherapist. In Britain, this is still unusual. Nevertheless, it could be argued that with the "nuclear family" of two adults and two children, there is much less support than in an extended family of relatives within easy reach. Thus, there is possibly more sources of stress and less help in coping with problems. In this setting, **any other person (therapist or counsellor) who can identify an individual's sources of stress and increase the individual's ability to cope will be of great benefit**. Essentially, with an extended family there is perhaps less stress and more resources to cope with any stress. Thus, the ease with which individuals move around the country for attractive jobs results in small families; these individuals then depend on the therapist or counsellor rather than the older generation of the family.

3. Hypnotherapy

The classical scenario of a patient visiting his hypnotherapist is one of pleasant surroundings with the patient lying on a couch. The patient is unwinding in a relaxed position. Hypnotism takes the individual into a deeper relaxation – "a nervous sleep". It is not like natural sleep and behaviour can be changed in this state of "neurhypnotism", later abbreviated to plain "hypnotism". In the hypnotic state, individuals do not lose control of the mind and cannot be made to do what they do not want to do. Instead, **the hypnotic state is a state of altered awareness in which individuals can focus and be receptive** to suggestions of the hypnotist.

It is possible for individuals to learn self-hypnosis. This has the great advantage of allowing the individual more control of stressful situations. Greatest success with hypnosis is obtained in those individuals who have high motivation, an open mind and are prepared to put time and effort into acquiring this skill.

Auto-suggestion changes an individual's attitudes by positive suggestion. It could be regarded as a milder form of hypnosis. Undoubtedly, there is a great strength in positive suggestions. The most famous is perhaps: "Every day, in every way, I am getting better and better".

If the above suggestion is repeated constantly throughout the day, it will probably influence the subconscious. Like hypnotic suggestions, **the positive statement produces a better result** compared to the negative. Thus, it is better to say "I shall........" rather than "I shall not........". Also, it is best to avoid "I will try........." as this leaves open the opportunity to fail.

4. Biofeedback

It is not surprising that in the West a science-based approach to unwinding should be developed. The basis of biofeedback is as follows: the individual does not usually become aware of stress; so, **if a machine can make the individual aware of stress, then the individual would be able to control the stress**. Thus, an individual's increased stress often results in increased sweating which could be measured in terms of the skin's resistance to electricity. A small, portable instrument which monitors such activity would allow an individual to control sweating and thus the stress. Muscle tension is another measurement which is amenable to instrumentation.

Although it makes an excellent story, the early, good results of biofeedback have been difficult to repeat. Reality is probably that several processes control any one end-result. Thus, for example, it may be possible to reduce sweating without reducing stress. Nevertheless, if an individual is aware of a problem (such as increased sweating which may mean greater tension) avoidance action can be instigated. Perhaps the greatest merit of biofeedback is that it emphasizes the role of the patient in determining the outcome of his/her situation.

Visualization is the development of a normal process. Many people have attempted to prepare for a difficult situation by first rehearsing the situation in their imagination. This could be a meeting to end a relationship, or a job interview. We are all also aware of the power of our own thoughts. Thus, "I'm looking forward to the evening" means a lot more than "I'm dreading the evening". The Buddhists have used visualization in their metta meditations. Visualization has apparently been successful in the treatment of cancer. Individuals have been reported to visualize a giant eraser which slowly rubs out their cancer. This process is repeated many times during the day and there have been many documented remissions from cancer. Some practitioners have emphasized that if visualization can affect cancer it must be far easier for the technique to enhance unwinding.

SUMMARY

1. The history of unwinding can be traced to Eastern attitudes where there is an emphasis on being passive; whereas in the West there is an emphasis on being active.

2. In Buddhism, individuals develop insight and awareness into their lives, with the extinction of an individual's need to do, to get, to achieve and to have material things.

3. Taoism is about living in peace with oneself and one's environment.

4. Japanese Zen involves the practice of meditation under strict rules.

5. In Yoga, the object is to unite the body, mind and emotions for a harmonious life.

6. Christianity is based on the life of Jesus Christ, and through prayer it is possible for an individual to know God.

7. Psychotherapy is the process in which sources of anxiety or stress are identified.

8. Hypnotherapy ("nervous sleep") is a deeper relaxation in which behaviour can be influenced. Autosuggestion changes an individual's behaviour by positive suggestion.

9. Biofeedback is a science based approach to unwinding. Visualization is the process by which an individual visualizes a problem and its removal.

CHAPTER FIVE
PLAN TO UNWIND

Robert, an old aged pensioner, was famous in the village. His major attribute was the ability to go to sleep mid-way during the minister's sermon. Just as the minister was getting into top gear and pounding the pulpit with his fists, Robert's snoring could be heard like a foghorn. It was loud and spasmodic, thus causing maximum disruption to the minister's sermon. Soon, the high point of the sermon for the congregation was when Robert would start to snore. One day, the minister had an inspired idea. He took Robert's grandson Alex aside and said to him:

"If you can keep your Grandfather awake during the sermon, I shall pay you twenty pence!"

This sounded like easy money to Alex and amazingly, during the sermon on the next Sunday, there was no snoring. The good news continued for the rest of the month. Then, suddenly, during the family service the next month, Robert's snoring bellowed out to the delight of the children and the congregation.

The minister was aghast and took Alex aside:

"Your Grandad went to sleep today. I shall not be paying you twenty pence."

"No bother," Alex replied. "My Grandad is paying me fifty pence not to keep him awake."

The ability to sleep is a blessing. The need for the body to rest is the fourth commandment: "Six days you shall labour, and do all your work...... and rested the seventh day" (Exodus, 20. 9).

The ability to unwind is a skill which requires time and effort before the individual becomes competent. This time and effort will be amply rewarded, but the skill is not easy to develop.

In this chapter, the plan to unwind will be stated. Unlike many other unwinding techniques, it does not require the presence of a teacher. However, it does demand motivation from the reader and a willingness to learn. If the reader is prepared to spend time and effort in the development of the skill of unwinding, there will be many mental and physical benefits.

THE PLAN

The plan has five stages:

1. Entrance
2. Muscles
3. Breathing
4. Mind
5. Exit

The initial letters of the five stages spell **"EMBME"**. Embme is a palindrome. A palindrome is a word or phrase, the letters of which when taken in reverse order read the same. Embme is also an aid to the memory. It will allow the reader to remember what the stages are and what is the next stage.

STAGE ONE: ENTRANCE

The entrance into the Plan to unwind is important. Some indiviuals benefit from having a long, hot bath before starting the session. The reader must take great care to ensure that several conditions are present. Success of the Plan depends on these initial preparations. Thus, there must be:

i) enough time

Although this is quite an obvious requirement, it is surprising how many people do not consider it. **The Plan takes at least half an hour** and during this time there should be no interruptions. A television commercial break is insufficient time. It is also not wise to try and squeeze the Plan in between two other appointments. When a person is experienced with the Plan this is possible, but it should not be tried in the early stages of learning the Plan.

ii) mental commitment

This is perhaps the most important initial requirement. Success is limited if you are busy thinking about other matters rather than on the Plan. It is best, for half an hour, to really try and concentrate on making the Plan work. During this period, other worries should be forgotten. Say to yourself:

"I really want to become good at the Plan and I will try my hardest to develop these skills".

iii) a quiet place

It is not possible to unwind with the radio or television on, at least not until the technique has been fully mastered. **A quiet place allows greater concentration**. Although there should not be any distracting noises in the room, it does not matter if there is noise outside, such as the passing traffic on the road outside. If there is a telephone in the room, take it off the hook or unplug it. Some individuals are helped by non-distracting music, or sounds from nature such as bird songs or running water.

iv) comfort

Comfort is influenced by many factors. The room must be sufficiently warm with no cold draughts. As you unwind you become colder and if you start shivering, you are not going to make progress. Some individuals prefer to lie down, whereas others prefer to sit. **Sitting in a firm chair with a good back and arm supports is probably best**. If you choose to lie down, the floor is better than a bed. When you have found your place and position, consider your clothing. Tight clothes inhibit the process of unwinding. Loosen your tie and belt. If shoes are tight, take them off or loosen the laces.

v) concentration

In some forms of meditation the eyes are kept partly open and focussed on an object. Paintings and mystical diagrams (yantras and mandelas) are well- established aids to Eastern meditation. A simpler aid is a lighted candle in a darkened room. One problem with such objects is that the individual may become dependant on the object to unwind. As unwinding is aimed at providing independence rather than dependence, such objects are not recommended. For the Plan in this book,

the eyes should be closed. The act of closing the eyes is also symbolic, and allows the individual to shut out the world and turn inwards. In addition, with the eyes closed, visual distractions are reduced and it is possible to have greater concentration. Some individuals have difficulty keeping their eyes closed and these may benefit from the use of a blindfold.

STAGE TWO: MUSCLES

Tension readily builds up in muscles and it is important to be aware of particular areas of tension such as the shoulders and neck. The unwinding Plan involves checking that all the major muscle groups are not tense. Although it is possible to consider small muscle groups, with the Plan larger groups of muscles are considered. This approach allows easier recall and can achieve the same effects. **In the Plan, you work up the body with five large muscle areas, in the following order: legs, abdomen, arms, shoulders and face.**

With each large area, the muscles are contracted until the tension can be felt, usually while you count up to ten. Next, relax and enjoy the wonderful sensation of the muscles unwinding as you count up to twenty. Then, move on to the next muscle area. The best approach to contracting the muscle areas is as follows:

i) **legs:** press the whole leg downwards onto the floor.

ii) **abdomen**: contract your tummy muscles, and at the same

54

time, you will notice that your chest muscles will also tighten.

iii) **arms:** press the whole arm downwards onto the chair's arm support or onto the floor, and at the same time make a fist with your hands.

iv) **shoulders:** raise these up in the direction of the top of your head, and you will notice that the neck muscles tighten.

v) **face:** try and screw up your face by closing your eyes so tightly that your cheeks go upwards.

It is easy to remember the large muscle areas because you are essentially working up the body from the legs. After you have finished with the muscles of the face, try and enjoy all of the muscles in your body slowly unwinding. Slowly count up to fifty and then proceed to the next stage, breathing.

STAGE THREE: BREATHING

Although everyone breathes every minute of every day, many are not aware of the importance of breathing. **Breathing also reflects an individual's state of mind**: quiet and regular when relaxed; noisy and irregular when excited; and even no breathing when there is fear or apprehension. Not surprisingly, there is a whole school of yoga devoted to the control of breathing.

You should **breathe through the nose** rather than through

the mouth. This is because the nose has protective mechanisms, such as hairs to remove dirt and infectious agents. If you cannot breathe through your nose because of an infection, then breathe through your mouth. However, you must remember that breathing through the mouth is a temporary measure.

In stage three, you should:

i) **breathe in fully** so that you cannot take in any more air, then hold the position whilst you count from one to three.

ii) **breathe out fully** so that there is no air left in the chest and then hold the position whilst you count from one to three.

iii) **repeat** (i) and (ii) three times.

iv) **breathe naturally**, which usually means about half of the breaths in (i) and (ii). Your breathing should be quiet, regular and natural. You should not have to concentrate on breathing. Your breathing should be slow and gentle as it would be whilst you are sleeping. Count up to fifty and then proceed to Stage Four.

STAGE FOUR: MIND CONTROL

This is the heart of unwinding, and the stage which demands the biggest commitment from the individual. By this stage, the muscles have become unwound and now it is the time for unwinding the mind. Unfortunately, the mind is much more resistant to control. Control can only be achieved by the use of powerful mind tricks:

1. Peaceful scenes

Once the muscles are unwound, the mind usually starts to wander. The mind is not unlike a young puppy running loose. It darts from one object to another. The aim is to try and put a lead on the puppy. Such control can be achieved by **concentrating on a peaceful scene**. This may be an empty beach at sunrise, a peaceful lake, a waterfall or whatever scene brings you the greatest tranquility. It can be a great help if you have a picture of this scene. Such pictures can be referred to and produce unwinding without going through the full Plan. It is also useful if you have several peaceful scenes. On some days a particular scene may be more helpful to your mood on that day. Some people benefit from seeing a more abstract scene such as the giant spring unwinding you on the front cover of this book.

2. Removing intruders

Despite your attempt to control your mind with peaceful scenes, other thoughts will intrude into your mind. When this happens **you need to remove these intrusive thoughts**. This is achieved by your visualizing the new thought on the sand of a clear beach. Then you slowly remove this new thought by pouring sand over it. Soon the new thought has disappeared under the sand. Another technique is to visualize the new thought on the sand and then allow the tide to come in until the thought is removed by the sea.

3. Mantra

A **mantra** is the sound form of God. The word can be more generally used to represent a sound which helps a person to unwind. It also concentrates the mind and prevents the intrusion of other thoughts. Several words can be used, such as "unwind", "relax", "peace". It is useful for you to choose a word which you can repeat when other thoughts intrude on your unwinding. A good word is the one that reminds you of the stages of unwinding "embme". Again, several words can be kept for such situations. **Like the visual techniques for removing intrusive thoughts, it is also useful to have certain words (mantras) which can be repeated to remove intruding thoughts**.

When you start to learn to unwind you would have done well to keep your mind on a peaceful scene for five minutes. You probably would have needed to use the visual and sound removal techniques for intrusive thoughts. You can now proceed to stage five of unwinding.

As you become more experienced at unwinding, this stage of mind control can be used to greater benefit. It is a time when you can try and understand your life. Then, you can analyse the problems in your life and attempt to find solutions. These aspects of mind control are so important that the next two chapters have been devoted to the Understanding and Control of life (Chapters Six and Seven). However, before you can incorporate the information in Chapter Six you must have practised the Plan at least one hundred times on separate occasions. Some individuals may choose not to attempt greater mind control. Indeed, many are happy with the benefits of unwinding without attempting to do more.

Some individuals fall asleep during the fourth stage. Do not worry. This is quite common and is a good sign. Indeed, many patients use the first four stages to go to sleep. After all, **sleep is the ultimate unwinding process**. In time, you will develop control of whether you allow yourself to sleep or not. If you do sleep, try and apply stage five to your awakening.

STAGE FIVE: EXIT

After you have had a session of unwinding, it is important to finish the session properly. Indeed, **the type of exit can influence the benefit from the unwinding exercise**. In this respect, our best teachers are animals and young children. When awakening from sleep, they do not usually jump up, do twenty press- ups, dress in thirty seconds and go out in five minutes. Instead, they savour the experience of getting up. **The exit from unwinding is also an experience to enjoy**.

First, open your eyes and slowly look around the whole room. Appreciate your surroundings. Next, have a good deep yawn, you will need the extra oxygen to get up. Then, stretch the arms and the legs at the same time. Try and enjoy being able to move again. Slowly get out of the chair or off the ground. Yawn and stretch at the same time. Finally, shout out your mantra, "Embme!", with great gusto. Now, you are ready to take on the entire world.

Stage Five is also an excellent way to get up after sleep. It can increase the benefits from sleep. Indeed, it is a natural process which can ensure you have a good start to the day.

APPLICATION

How many times should you use the Plan to unwind? The simple answer is "Often". For the very best results, unwinding should be an integral part of your life. It is like food. You do not ask :

"How often should I eat?"

Yet, it is a similar question. Ideally you should unwind as often as you eat.

Like food, it is best to have several meals rather than one mammoth meal. Similarly, **best results are obtained when an individual is able to unwind once a day** rather than once a week on Sunday. It is most important to be regular. Once a day for half an hour is a hundred times better than six hours on Sunday.

60

Again, **at times of great stress**, it is best to have unwinding sessions scattered throughout the day. The best results are obtained when one is able to have a session in mid-morning, mid-afternoon and mid-evening. Obviously, this is not practical, or even necessary for many individuals. However, **if you are unwell or suffering from severe stress, it is the approach that will result in the greatest benefit**.

SUMMARY

1. The Plan to unwind has five stages: entrance, muscles, breathing, mind, and exit. The first letters spell **"EMBME"** which is an aid to recall the stages.

2. Stage one (entrance) requires enough time, mental commitment, a quiet place, comfort and concentration.

3. Stage two (muscles) involves a methodical process of tensing and relaxing muscles in the following order: legs, abdomen, arms, shoulders, and face.

4. Stage three (breathing) is achieved by breathing in fully, breathing out fully, three times, and then breathing in half breaths slowly, gently and naturally.

61

5. Stage four (mind control) requires the use of several mind tricks: peaceful scenes, removing intruders, and a mantra.

6. Stage five (exit) is important and cannot be hurried. This should be an enjoyable stage with a slow return to normal life.

7. Regular and frequent application of the Plan achieves best results.

CHAPTER SIX
UNDERSTAND LIFE

The teacher was making a great effort to explain to her young pupils that subtraction was easy.

"To subtract, you must remember that you must first have things of the same kind. You cannot take four oranges from five bananas, or three pears from six apples. It must be four oranges from five oranges, or three pears from six pears. Also, you must take away a smaller number from a bigger number. Is this clear?"

It seemed simple and all of the children seemed to understand. Even young Colan was nodding his head as he continued to bite his pencil. Suddenly his eyes opened wide and he stopped breathing. He had had an idea. He bit hard on the pencil and raised his hand. His teacher was exasperated, but managed to say:

"What is it Colan? We have a lot to do and we must not waste

63

any more time."

"I'm sorry," replied Colan, "but how can a farmer take five pints of milk from one cow?"

The above story is quite typical of life. It is easy to identify with the teacher, to understand her rules for subtraction and to agree with her. Also, it is simple and that is how it should be. Then, the Colans of this world complicate matters. Colan was speaking from his understanding of life. All he said was correct. Nevertheless, if the teacher and Colan were correct, there is still a lot that needs to be explained. This story is characteristic of life. Something appears to be simple and straightforward, then suddenly it becomes complicated and makes your brain hurt. You are happy, standing next to the road as the cars go by, then suddenly a car drives into a puddle of water and you are covered with dirt and disbelief on your face.

As usual, the anwer is simple. It always is when you have been told. This is one of the facts of life. It is also something that should give you encouragement. **All problems have solutions; you can learn to find solutions to your problems**. The answer is that the teacher was correct. However, the teacher was also attempting to give her pupils some rules for subtraction. Therefore, it is not possible to physically take away something from something else unless it is of the same kind. Colan was also correct. The confusion arose because the teacher's rules were inadequate for Colan's example.

It was possible for the farmer to take five pints of milk from the one cow because the cow had five pints of milk. The cow also had many pounds of meat, a head, two ears, a nose, four feet et-cetera. Thus, as the cow is composed of many parts, it is possible for one to take things from any of these parts. Obviously, it is not possible to take apples from a cow as apples are not part of a cow. Also, if the cow does not have milk, it is not possible to take five pints of milk from the cow. A general word (such as cow) which covers many things (such as possession of milk, meat etc) can therefore cause confusion. Most confusion is caused by misunderstanding because of the use of words.

LIFE

Life is a frequently misunderstood word. It can be seen as "activity", "vitality", "energy" and "get-up-and-go". Although life is all of these things, it is more simply the opposite of death. However, most individuals tend to associate life with the good things. For some, it is because they see the bad things of life as being "negative". This may be true if you can see only the bad things. **The ideal is to see life as it is**. What is required is a great deal of honesty and the ability to see yourself as others see you.

Another misunderstood word is stress. Stress can be seen as "anxiety", "burden", "oppression" or "hassle". It is only these things, if you let it be. More realistically, stress is part of life; it is a necessary part of living. Like the weather, it can be for good or bad. Many have the misconception that the ideal life is one without stress. This is like saying that the ideal life is one where the weather is always good. Sadly, this would not be the real world but an artificial one. In the real world, the ideal life is where one can cope with the weather and be happy.

Similarly, stress is part of living. The ideal situation is where one can cope with stress and be happy. A good definition is: **stress is a process in which the resources of the person are matched against the demands of the environment.** This definition is repeated from Chapter Two because it is very important. Stress is a very simple balance between your resources and those of your environment. The environment is composed of those around you (family and friends) and situations that you are in (job and finances). If the demands of the environment are greater than your resources you will be unhappy, anxious and even unwell. **An understanding of life involves obtaining information about yourself, and being able to identify problems.**

OBTAIN INFORMATION

The ability to obtain information about yourself is a skill. **You need to see the truth and not what you would like life to be.** Human beings have a great capacity to ignore the truth, and impose their own wishes on others. This could simply involve insisting that your teenage children will like the clothing that you have bought them, or that the whole family will enjoy watching an old film that you like. In a more complicated matter, you could convince yourself that the job that you have is the best job for you, that once you have paid off the loan on the car, you will be happy. As these are familiar and common situations, how can you be sure that you are seeing life as it is – understanding life?

The answer is in information. Scientists are trained to collect information and they recognize two broad groups of information: subjective and objective. **Subjective** information depends on how the subject is feeling, such as deciding the temperature on whether the subject is hot or cold. **Objective** information does not depend on the feelings of the subject, but usually on some other measurement, such as using a thermometer to decide on the temperature. Obviously, objective information is usually more dependable than subjective information. Nevertheless, there are many emotions, such as love or jealousy, which are difficult to measure objectively. So, how do you obtain information on yourself?

In the past, before the days of barriers at level crossings, there was always a large sign where the road crossed the railway tracks. The sign would read: **"STOP, LOOK, LISTEN!"** . This was good advice and probably saved many a life. It is also the best way of obtaining good information.

1. Stop

The first objective is to **STOP**. The Plan to unwind (Chapter Five), achieves this as its end-result. You will effectively have put the brakes on your life for a short time. In the Game of living, everyone needs some time when they are spectators rather than participants. It is like embarking on a 500 mile car drive. There is a great need for frequent stops, time to unwind, and perhaps assess progress. In this way, fewer wrong turnings are made, and the whole trip can be an enjoyable adventure.

Many individuals try and combine several jobs. Thus, they assess their progress whilst they are continually moving. For some this is possible, but for most the chances of mistakes are dramatically increased. This should not be a revelation. It just makes sense that it is easier to drink coffee when the car is stationary; and, it is more likely that coffee will be spilled if you drink whilst driving. Drinking coffee is relatively unimportant, but obtaining good information about yourself influences your happiness and health.

2. Look

In the Plan to unwind (Chapter Five), mind control was the fourth stage. However the greatest value of this stage is that it can allow you to understand life by obtaining information about yourself, identify problems and solve these problems. Naturally, **these objectives are not easily obtained and are advanced phases of mind control**. They are too ambitious for the individual who is starting to learn the Plan. However, if you have practiced the Plan to unwind on at least one hundred separate occasions, it is reasonable for you to proceed with these phases of mind control.

The **ability to look at yourself is a valuable skill**, and allows you to gain some information about yourself. In this phase, you give your mind limited freedom. You let your mind wander through your day for the time it takes to slowly count to twenty, and then you come back to your peaceful scene, and also repeat your mantra. Try and look at how you have spent the day: was it a good day? was it a difficult day? was it a happy day? was there a problem? In this way, you will obtain a lot of information about the day. It is not unlike the questions you might ask a child after a day at school. Sometimes, your mind quickly focusses on a problem or emotional situation which has overshadowed the day. Do not worry, this is quite normal. Do not return to your peaceful scene and mantra. Instead, proceed to problem identification and problem solving which are considered separately, later in this Chapter. When you look at your life objectively, you will find a tug of war between the demands of the environment and your personal resources (Chapter Seven).

3. Listen

The skill of listening to others is a great asset. Many individuals are so busy talking that there is no time to listen. Others like to listen to only good news. Both of these attitudes are equally wrong. The reason that they are so frequently adopted is probably because these attitudes are positive. They are also active, and do not allow bad news to discourage the individual. Whilst such a result has some advantages, the greatest disadvantage is that it prevents the individual from seeing the truth.

There is an old saying: **"People tend to see you better than you are or worse than you are, never as you are"**. As you have the potential to have more accurate information about yourself than anyone else, it is up to you to see yourself as you are. The main consideration is not to be too discouraged about the horrible (often incorrect) things that are said about you; nor to believe the wonderful (often incorrect) things that are said about you. Nevertheless, you must listen to what people say.

The good news is that you have a time advantage. In the vast majority of situations, people will be talking about what you have done. This time-lag is a tremendous advantage. You know what you have done, and thus others talking about you is in part predictable. In addition, you can be prepared for the worst. The same goes for the good news. Thus, **what is said about you should not be a surprise**. If it is and it happens a lot you do not see yourself as others see you.

Much of the philosophy of understanding life in this book is in the quite superb poem **"IF", by Rudyard Kipling**. It has so much good sense in it that I feel compelled to quote it in its entirety:

"If you can keep your head when all about you
Are losing theirs and blaming it on you,
If you can trust yourself when all men doubt you,
But make allowance for their doubting too;
If you can wait and not be tired by waiting,
Or being lied about, don't deal in lies,
Or being hated, don't give way to hating,
And yet don't look too good, nor talk too wise:

If you can dream-and not make dreams your master;
If you can think – and not make thoughts your aim;
If you can meet with Triumph and Disaster
And treat those two imposters just the same;
If you can bear to hear the truth you've spoken
Twisted by knaves to make a trap for fools,

Or watch the things you gave your life to, broken,
And stoop to build'em up with worn-out tools;

If you can make one heap of all your winnings
And risk it at one turn of pitch-and-toss,
And lose, and start again at your beginnings
And never breathe a word about your loss;
If you can force your heart and nerve and sinew
To serve your turn long after they are gone,
And so hold on when there is nothing in you
Except the Will which says to them "Hold on!"

If you can talk with crowds and keep your virtue,
Or walk with Kings – nor lose the common touch,
If neither foes nor loving friends can hurt you,
If all men count with you, but none too much;
If you can fill the unforgiving minute
With sixty seconds' worth of distance run,
Yours is the Earth and everything that's in it.
And – which is more – you'll be a Man, my son!"

IDENTIFY PROBLEMS

Problems do not suddenly materialise as massive and
overwhelming. The usual scenario is a small problem is
overlooked until it becomes a large problem. Sometimes, it can
be ignored as a large problem, but when it becomes massive
it cannot be ignored. It is easy to avoid cutting the grass, but
when you cannot see out of the window, a small problem has

become a massive one. Thus, the secret is to **deal with problems when they are small**. This requires an excellent surveillance system as one needs to be very aware to see problems early. There are three components to this system: be aware of emotions, recognize changes in health and ask questions.

1. Emotions

Whilst you are practising the Plan to unwind, stage four (mind control) allows you the opportunity to assess your day. After your peaceful scene and your mantra, let your mind wander through the day. Often the mind goes quickly to an emotional situation, such as an argument with a spouse or colleague, do not return to your peaceful scene and mantra. Instead, attempt to identify the problem underneath your emotional reaction.

Anger, frustration, jealousy, resentment and fear are all very strong emotions. They can be regarded as a warning light that there is an underlying problem. The solution is to try and identify the problem and solve it. Yet, many are so involved in living and re-living the emotional scene that there is no time to identify and solve the problem. **The emotion is not the problem; the problem is hidden under the emotion.**

2. Health

It is easy to take health for granted. It is also easy to ignore minor ill health. Thus, difficulty sleeping, tiredness, depression and heartburn may be ignored. However, they are early-warning signals. If they are not acted upon, more worrying complaints such as chest pain or panic attacks may develop. These, too, may be ignored, but if you keep driving through red traffic lights, it is only a matter of time before a disaster occurs. Health problems are considered in more detail in Chapter Eight (Be Better).

At this stage, it is important to remember that your **personal problems may result in ill health**. In many natural disasters, this statement is totally acceptable. Thus, everyone would accept that an individual may be burned in a fire. However, many individuals are unable to link abdominal pain with a personal problem. Although this is not surprising, it is only a reflection of the limited experience of most individuals.

3. Questions

Parents often reprimand their children for asking too many questions, and this may be one explanation of the reluctance of adults to ask themselves questions. Yet, the ability to ask questions is invaluable in being able to identify problems. Thus, if you had an argument with a spouse or colleague, to identify the problem you may need to ask several questions: why did it happen? how did you behave? how did they behave? who was right? how do you feel now?

The words of Rudyard Kipling show great insight into the art of asking questions:

"I keep six honest serving men (they taught me all I know);

Their names are What and Why and When And How and Where and Who".

As you obtain answers to these questions, try to identify the main problem. Often there are many other mitigating factors such as you/they are tired, you/they were rushed, you/they misinterpreted what was said/done, or you/they overreacted. **Always attempt to see the other person's point of view**. Put yourself in their position.

Lastly, always finish your questions with one that summarises the position, such as, how unhappy/happy am I with the situation? After your unwinding session (which may take 1-1½ hours if you are solving a difficult problem), it is helpful to summarise the session on a piece of paper. Write down your single question (and any additional ones) and your solutions. Look at them carefully and see if you still agree with your choice. Sometimes solutions look different when written on paper.

The ability to make decisions about your problem is part of being able to control life and is considered in Chapter Seven (Control Life). Although the skill to solve your problems is regarded as a great gift, it cannot be done without the ability to obtain information about yourself and to identify your problems.

SUMMARY

1. All problems have solutions; you can learn to find solutions to your problems.

2. Stress is part of life. It is a process in which the resources of the person are matched against the demands of the environment.

3. To understand life involves obtaining information about yourself, and being able to identify your problems.

4. Good information about yourself is obtained if you can stop, look and listen. The skill to stop and look are advanced phases of mind control. Similarly, the skill of listening to others can be difficult to acquire.

5. The early identification of problems allows them to be dealt with whilst they are still small. You need a surveillance system to identify problems early: awareness of emotions; a recognition of changes in health; and the ability to ask yourself questions.

CHAPTER SEVEN
CONTROL LIFE

It was a cold, windy and wet morning when the door bell rang. Cicely opened the door and greeted the man outside. He was conducting a survey on how people spent their money, and was relieved when Cicely invited him into the warm house. She quickly made a pot of tea as the gentleman got out his list of questions. Although he had imposed himself on Cicely, he somehow blamed her for the bad weather. He was not in a good mood. He started:

"Do you work?"

"No," Cicely replied. "I'm a housewife."

The man was a bit annoyed at her not having to work, but proceeded to his next question:

"How do you spend your money?"

"Well, that's easy," Cicely quickly answered. "Three-quarters is spent on food, 20% on the house, 20% on clothes, 30% on the grandchildren and 5% on the hamster."

The man started to write this down and then with a look of frustration shouted: "It adds up to 150%! It is impossible!!"

Cicely was totally relaxed as she looked at her angry, wet visitor. With great control, she replied:

"No, it is not. I buy only at the sales."

Those individuals who have most control of life are like Cicely. They seem to have more time; they seem to accomplish more. When you look at what they have done and you add it up, it always seems impossible. How can this be? Well, first, it is obviously not impossible. However, like everything else, **to control life, you need to develop a skill**. The development of this skill requires time and effort, but is not impossible. There are three important considerations: use of time, the reward/effort ratio and decision-making.

USE OF TIME

Time can be short for all that should be done. Modern life also consumes time with non-productive activities such as travelling to and from work. Work itself may be dreadfully boring with long hours; the majority work for money and not for love. Thus, it is quite understandable that **there is not enough time for most**

individuals to do what they want to do. Some people solve this problem by trying to save some time. Their efforts may involve travelling faster, having less sleep, missing meals or spending less time with the family. Sadly, all of these solutions also have adverse consequences of their own. **The solution is not to waste time.**

Although this solution seems simple, it is very difficult to apply in practice. The reason is that most individuals do not know: what they need to do; what they want to do; and the priorities of the work around them. Thus, time can be wasted on jobs that they do not need or want to do. Often such jobs were just there and got caught up with the rush, for example the car is automatically washed on Sunday without assessing if the car needs a wash, or if you want to do it. Similarly, many do work with low priority and then rush work with high priority; mistakes are more easily made, and time is wasted in repeating work.

1. Your needs

Your needs can be divided into three large groups: those common to all human beings; those common to many people; and those common to very few people, possibly only yourself.

It is instructive how few needs are common to all human beings. Obviously, there are the needs to eat, to sleep and to be happy. However, other needs are much less common. Thus, the need to work or to earn money are critically important to some individuals, but are actively avoided by others. In today's society the media and the advertising industry are great influences on people's lives. Such influences can make individuals feel that there are needs, when in fact no needs exist. **You need to identify your own needs; the needs of others do not necessarily apply to you.**

Some needs are easily overlooked. They may be capable of having a dramatic effect on those concerned, and when overlooked the consequences may be serious. Some of these needs such as privacy or personal space are usually taken for granted. Individuals deprived of these may be unaware that such deprivation may produce illness.

The needs that are most important for your individuality are those which are common to few people. As they apply to only a few, the media or advertisements do not give such needs great exposure. It is therefore even more easy to overlook these needs. In large groups, when individual needs are neglected, everyone in the group can become very much like everyone else. When everyone is almost the same, with passage of time, there is less individual happiness. Therefore, you should try and identify your individual needs (such as a liking for a particular place, food or an unusual hobby).

To use time well, **most of your time must be spent on your needs**. The thinking is: time is limited and so should be spent on what you need. After you have done this, any remaining time can be spent on other matters.

2. Your wants

There is an important difference between "wants" and "needs".

Needs are necessary for your existence and happiness; whereas, wants are not necessary for your existence, but may make you more happy. Thus, owning a car is usually a want rather than a need. Although this last statement is generally true, there are exceptions. This is because needs and wants are individual. Occasionally, a want becomes a need, for example if someone uses a car in employment. As it can be difficult to separate wants from needs, many individuals do not attempt to do so.

The importance of being able to identify wants is that **time should not be spent on wants if there is not enough time for needs**. To say that all wants are needs is a common excuse to avoid having to use time well. Thus, people may say that learning French is something that they need to do; time is spent on learning French to the detriment of their work; and when they become unemployed they feel that the world is unfair. Suddenly the distinction becomes apparent: learning French was a want, the job was a need.

3. Priorities

When there is a separation of wants and needs, a further step has to be taken. There is frequently not enough time for all of the needs. Most people would accept that reasonable needs are: family, friends, job and finances. Yet, for example, there is often a choice to be made about time spent with the family, as opposed to time spent with friends. Thus, **you need to establish priorities among your needs**. Some needs are more important than others.

For many, the most important need is for the family, closely followed by finances. This assessment can easily cause confusion. For example, an individual devoted to earning money may say that by earning lots of money, the family are provided for. Although a common argument, this is a weak argument. The needs of a family are many, and money is only one, perhaps the least important need. Therefore, it is important that you spend time on the family's needs and then time on financial needs.

Another confusing factor is that **priorities change with time**. This is because your actions today influence your actions tomorrow. If you have spent time with the family today, you can spend time with friends tomorrow. In this way, as one need is met, you can satisfy another need. It is also important to remember that **priorities are dependent on situations**. If a member of your family is ill, you will obviously have to spend less time with your friends. Similarly, if you are acquiring a skill or a qualification, you will have to spend less time with family and friends.

The use of time is a difficult skill to acquire. It involves separating your needs from your wants; and establishing priorities for your needs. However, it would be a mistake to think that good use of time is always spent on needs. As life is about balances, this would be wrong. The message in this section is: to be able to control life, most time (not all) must be spent on needs and not wants.

REWARD/EFFORT RATIO

In Chapter Two (Why unwind?) it was stated that a great secret in the control of life was the reward/effort ratio. A ratio is one measure (in this case, reward) divided by another measure (in this case, effort). The reward/effort ratio is an excellent way of assessing the use of time. Thus, the **reward/effort ratio should be used to identify situations where there is maximum reward for minimal effort**. As minimal effort is involved, there is also less time used.

1. The System

Some individuals have found that the reward/effort ratio is a difficult system to apply. Although it is a different way of thinking, it is a skill that should be developed as the benefits of acquiring the skill are great. First, it is important to be able to think of "units". A unit is one of anything. Effort is considered in units of time (hours, days, weeks, months or years), and reward is considered in units of happiness (none, some, average, great or a lot). Therefore, **a situation which produces average reward for a little effort (a few hours) is much better than one which produces great reward for maximum effort (years)**. The reason is that you can acquire more units of reward in a given time (see Chapter Two).

Most people find it difficult to think in this way. Society today has perfection as its objective. Everyone seems conditioned to attempting to be "the best", "the winner". It seems bizarre for a population to be living millions of lives in an attempt to get into the "Guinness Book of Records". The analogy is with the Football Pools or National Lottery. **One cannot live a life in the hope of winning such prizes**, as by definition, the vast majority must be losers.

The sensible approach is one in which one is happy with many small prizes. In the vast majority of lives, it is possible for everyone to have many small prizes. These prizes give immediate happiness. It is the old example of the difference between "a bird in the hand as opposed to two birds in the bush". However, there is more. **When one achieves, one is more likely to achieve more**. Again, the old saying "Nothing succeeds as success". Thus the individual with many small prizes is better able to control life compared to the individual who is waiting for the big prize.

2. Results

It can be seen that the **reward/effort ratio is about results**. It is not about hopes, aspirations or long shots. Life can be regarded as a gamble, and the reward/effort ratio is about results rather than hopes. Yet, one should say it is not about success. Success is a favourable outcome of something which you attempt. In today's world, there are many things in which success is a reflection of opportunity or good fortune. Life can be divided into areas that are predictable and areas that cannot be predicted. **The reward/effort ratio is about the part of life that can be predicted**. Sometimes in this area of life, there is also some luck. When this happens, it is a bonus.

To assess how useful the reward/effort ratio may be to you is easy. Look at the last year and ask the question: how many times have you achieved what you wanted? If this has happened many times, you probably already practice a form of the reward/effort ratio. If you have not achieved many things that you wanted, you will probably find the reward/effort ratio to be extremely useful. It will allow you to have more control of your life.

3. The future

To look into the future is very difficult. It is impossible to be able to see the future all of the time, and so many individuals do not attempt the exercise. However, almost everyone has opinions of what will happen. Indeed, they would defend such opinions with great gusto; they would be prepared to argue and even to fight. These strong emotions are rarely used productively. If anyone can predict the future it is possible to gain financially from this knowledge. However, most individuals have opinions of the future, but are unable to benefit from this knowledge. The reason is that **most people do not appreciate the importance of time**.

The appreciation of time is the difference between the professionals and the amateurs. Anyone can predict that house prices will rise or that computers will become cheap. However, **what is important is when will this happen**. If one knew when, it is possible to benefit from the knowledge. It is not even relevant for you to be exact, a prediction within months would be sufficient for a great benefit.

Most people look upon the exercise of predicting the future as a waste of time. This is expected as most people are usually wrong. Yet, with experience it is possible to be right some of the time. If you are right one in four times, you are doing well. Indeed, it is possible for you to become a millionaire if you could be right one in four times, and get the timing right.

Apart from money, why should you try to predict the future? The answer is that it is practice for being able to assess your use of time with the reward/effort ratio. **The more times your timing of the future is correct, the more control you could have of your life.**

DECISION-MAKING

A decision is the end-result of a process of assessment. It is slightly different from the ability to solve problems. The difference is simply that **most problems have several solutions and decision-making is choosing one of these solutions.**

1. Solve problems

In the previous chapter, problems were identified during the fourth stage (mind control) of the Plan to unwind. As you become more adept at identifying problems, you will be aware of problems before your unwinding session. Indeed, individuals

85

often identify problems that occur during the day and keep them for their unwinding sessions. In this way, they are making their first decision about the problem – to keep it for later. Such an approach may be regarded as delaying tactics or procrastination by some; however, if the problem is addressed at an unwinding session within 48 hours, the delay is acceptable. Anyway, **the success of any approach to the solving of problems will be judged by the results**.

The skill in the ability to solve problems is improved if one takes a methodical approach to problems. A recommended procedure is:

i) Timescale

Firstly, **it is essential to know how much time you have to solve the problem**. It is always easier to solve problems when you have lots of time. In addition some problems need a little time, and others a lot of time. Try and allocate more time to a problem than you first think that it will need. Initially, this will be quite difficult, but as you develop the skill, it will be easier to assess how much time it will take to solve any particular problem.

ii) Single question

Hopefully, from the section on identifying problems you will now have the problem down to a single question which has to be answered. Unfortunately, **many individuals try to answer**

questions which are not single but multiple. Thus, a question, such as "Do I need to buy a new television?" may depend on the answers to other questions: "Is the old television working?" "Can I afford to buy a new television?" or "Do I want to spend the money on something else?". If your answer does not depend on the answers to other questions, you have a single question.

iii) More information

Generally, the more information that you have, the better is the solution to the problem. However, **there is a great temptation to delay making a decision until you have more information**. Also, in some cases decisions are not made because there is too much information. A practical approach is to decide on solutions in the light of the available information. In these cases, the solutions could be changed if there is dramatic, new information. For the majority of cases, the new information does not change the solutions.

iv) Choices

In attempting to answer a single question, it is helpful to suggest several solutions. Although this approach requires more effort, it is more likely to lead to the right decision. This is because **in finding several solutions, you have to look at the question from different points of view,** or with the emphasis on different aspects of the question. Often the best solution is a combination of two possible answers.

v) Decisions

Faced with several choices, you must now make a decision. At this stage, you need to consider how realistic some of your solutions are. It is very common for people to decide on a solution that is dependent on major miracles. It is also best that the solution is totally dependent on yourself. A solution that involves the help and cooperation of the family, friends, or the local community are less likely to be successful. Thus, **the best solution is usually one that is practical and depends on your efforts**.

With solutions that involve a major change of habit (such as drinking, smoking, overeating), it is often best to attempt a little at a time. Thus, the solution to stopping smoking may not be "I shall never smoke again", but instead "I shall not smoke today!" Such a solution repeated every day is far more likely to succeed.

2. Good decisions

Why do some people make good decisions, whilst others make terrible decisions? To some extent, **good decisions are dependent on an individual's experience**. However, as a decision must be right for that person, a good decision for one person is not necessarily a good decision for another. Thus, experience is a small consideration. Nevertheless, like all skills, to make good decisions depends on several factors:

i) Fear of being wrong

This factor can be very inhibiting. It is a vicious circle: if you make bad decisions, you are likely to be wrong; if you are afraid of being wrong, you are likely to make bad decisions. Alternatively, if you are accustomed to making good decisions, you are less likely to be afraid of being wrong.

ii) Priorities

All questions are not equally important. You must be able to spend most time on the question that is important and urgent. However, as one makes better and better decisions, most time is spent on questions that are important and not urgent. It is quite a skill to know which problem to tackle first. This question is further explored in Chapter Seven (Control Life).

iii) Easy/difficult problems

When faced with a difficult problem, life can come to a stop. At the same time, you may have several easy problems, but the enormity of the difficult problem can paralyse you into inaction. The best approach is to solve the easy problems first. Quite surprisingly, the difficult problem often becomes less when you have solved several other easy problems. Lastly, it is a good idea to attempt difficult problems when you are fresh. A problem on Friday afternoon is often less daunting early on Monday morning.

iv) No regrets

Good decisions are easy to live with. Bad decisions should be regarded as learning exercises; try and see why you made a bad decision. Also, there should be no regrets about bad decisions. Too many people live their lives regretting decisions that they made in the past. Paradoxically, to make good decisions one must be able to live with the results of bad decisions. Again, it is worth emphasizing that decisions are personal. Therefore, **as long as a decision is right for you, do not be concerned about what others may say or feel**.

SUMMARY

1. Control of life involves: use of time, the reward/effort ratio and decision-making.

2. The essence of good use of time is not to waste time. You must be aware of your needs, wants and priorities.

3. Your needs are those things that are necessary for your existence and happiness. You need to identify your own needs; the needs of others do not necessarily apply to you.

4. Your wants are not necessary for your existence and **may**

make you happier. Time should not be spent on your wants if there is not enough time for your needs.

5. You need to establish priorities among your needs. Priorities change with time and situations.

6. The reward/effort ratio should be used to identify situations where there is maximum reward for minimal effort.

7. In solving problems, you must: know the timescale; identify a single question; know if more information is required; find several solutions to the problem; and make a decision.

8. For good decisions you must: have no fear of being wrong; recognize priorities; identify easy/difficult problems; and have no regrets about your decision.

CHAPTER EIGHT
BE BETTER

Gregory, Douglas and Martin were three middle-aged men who were being interviewed on television. The television programme was about health and people's reactions to sickness. The interviewer asked the question:

"If you were told by a doctor that you had only a month to live, what would you do?"

Douglas was the first to answer:

"This would be really bad news. I would sell my house and all of my possessions. With the money, I would travel the world and really enjoy my last month."

Martin was shaking his head in disbelief at this irresponsible attitude, he replied:

"I wouldn't behave like Douglas. My first responsibility would be to my family. I would make sure that all of my bills were paid and that my affairs were in order."

Gregory was also shaking his head in disagreement with his friends, he replied:

"Well, the first thing I would do is get a second opinion."

Gregory's point is very appropriate to health. When something is as important as health, it is wise to have more than one opinion. However, many individuals behave in a totally different way, and try to ignore their ill health. Why is this? There are perhaps two good reasons: people are afraid of illness and find it easier to pretend that minor illness does not exist; and secondly people hope that minor illness will go away on its own accord.

ILL HEALTH

Ill health can be defined as the opposite of well-being. Obviously, there can be very many causes of minor illnesses. In most cases these illnesses resolve spontaneously. However, it has been recently realised that very many minor illnesses may be produced by stress. These illnesses may resolve when the stress is absent, for example work stress may not produce symptoms at weekends. **If stress continues, minor illnesses may become serious with unremitting symptoms**. This section considers ill health due to stress in terms of minor illness, serious illness and its effects on pre-existing illness.

1. Minor illness

Stress can produce complaints in any system of the body. The following list is not exhaustive and is only intended to show the sort of symptoms that may be produced:

i) **central nervous system**: headaches, dizziness, insomnia, fatigue, anxiety, depression, reduced concentration.

ii) **cardiovascular system**: rapid pulse, palpitations, feeling of hotness, heaviness in chest, tingling in limbs.

iii) **respiratory**: difficulty breathing, wheeze, need to breathe quickly.

iv) **gastrointestinal**: changes in appetite, abdominal discomfort, diarrhoea, excess wind, a feeling of abdominal fullness, bloating after a meal.

v) **urinary**: need to pass urine frequently, dribbling.

vi) **genital**: impotence in men, reduced sexual urge in women.

vii) **musculoskeletal**: pains in joints, muscle pain, twitching of muscles.

All of the above symptoms can come and go. Their presence is related to the presence and extent of the stress. If stress continues, the number of complaints usually increase, and may become severe.

2. Serious illness

If stress is present for a long time, more serious illness may develop. One example is the Type A and Type B personalities. The Type A personality is very ambitious and competitive, with the need to accomplish and strives to succeed. The Type B personality is less ambitious, less competitive, more open to compromise and more able to relax. It is not surprising that Type A personalities are more prone to heart disease. Type A personalities are not exclusively business executives, but every occupation and social class has its Type A personalities.

Almost any complaint in the minor illness section may become chronic and more serious. However, serious illnesses which are common are: duodenal or stomach ulcers, colitis, asthma, depression and chronic anxiety. Continual stress may also produce more generalised problems such as skin rashes, or frequent infections.

3. Pre-existing illness

In patients who are already ill, stress can make matters worse. As mentioned above, cardiovascular disease is easily made worse by stress. Similarly, a variety of psychological disorders, such as anxiety and depression, can become worse. In these examples, removal or reduction in stress will result in a clinical improvement in the patient.

For some diseases, the patient's ultimate recovery may be prevented by high stress levels. Thus, for patients with irritable bowel syndrome or Post Viral Fatigue Syndrome (myalgic encephalomyelitis, Royal Free Disease, Chronic Fatigue Syndrome), stress is associated with relapse and the development of new symptoms. In these cases, **ultimate return to good health can be dependant on the removal or reduction of stress**.

Lastly, in another group of patients, the final removal of stress may not be accompanied by recovery. Presumably, these patients have become so damaged that it is not possible for them to return to normal. In minor degrees, this is seen as a result of living in modern cities. The more severe forms usually result as the aftermath of wars and other disasters. These individuals would have been unaffected if it had not been for these events, however their pre-existing personality may have predisposed them to such problems.

REDUCING STRESS

There are several ways individuals normally reduce stress. Most do not know why they are behaving in a particular way. This section considers such behaviour, and also the methods of reducing stress advocated in this book (unwinding, understanding and controlling life).

1. Behaviour

Exercise is perhaps the widest used method of reducing stress. The form of exercise (football, squash, hill-walking, or dancing) is not important. It is simply that the activity should totally occupy the mind, and so allow you to forget your stress. There is also the total physical exhaustion which can then be followed by sleep and relaxation. **The body greatly benefits from physical exercise**, and it is perhaps one of the best ways of reducing stress. Sadly, some individuals because of illness cannot indulge in physical exercise.

Good food is another excellent way of reducing stress. In many communities where stress is low, there is a great emphasis placed on the importance of food and its enjoyment. This is not usually the case in large cities where eating is rushed and tends to be "junk" food. These processed foods with additives, combined with high caffeine and sugar intake are by themselves able to produce stress. In addition, the end-result is an overweight individual. An individual's weight is a good indication of his/her general health.

Smoking, drug misuse and excessive alcohol consumption are all ways in which individuals try and reduce their stress. These methods work well initially, however they are addictive. The long-term consequences on the individual are illness, and eventually much greater stress. Their usefulness is strictly in short-term solutions to the need to reduce stress. These addictive habits can produce more problems than they solve.

2. Unwind

This is the best way of reducing stress. The Plan to unwind (Chapter Five: Plan to unwind) takes commitment, dedication, time and energy to learn. However, **the ability to unwind is a great skill in the game of living**. It allows you to immediately get away from your everyday worries and anxieties. Suddenly, you can be taken away from the turmoil of life, and be placed in a quiet oasis. You will be far away from everyone, in your own personal retreat. However, the ability to escape is only one advantage of being able to unwind.

Another great asset of unwinding is that it can be practiced by anyone, even those who have pre-existing illnesses and are not able to physically exercise. Exercise is such a common and important part of most people's lives that if exercise is not possible, most people feel incapacitated. For these individuals, unwinding can be a new world where they can be anything that they want. More importantly, the advanced phases of mind control (Chapter Six: Understanding Life, and Chapter Seven: Control Life) provide the opportunities to overcome their personal difficulties.

3. Understand

The great difficulty with stress is that **most people do not realise that they are under stress**. With the ability to unwind, there is an opportunity to obtain more information on your life. This information could lead to a greater understanding of the situations that you are in. Perhaps, the hardest step is understanding that there is stress in your life. When this is done, your subsequent actions are almost automatic. It is like when you walk into a darkened room, you cannot see and inevitably you bump into the furniture. As soon as you put the light on, you automatically avoid all of the obstacles. **To understand stress is like being able to put the light on**.

Another great stress reducing action is to identify problems that produce stress. When one has identified the problem, it is possible to take steps to reduce the impact of stress. Thus, you can be prepared for such problems (or avoid them). **For many problems, the simple process of their identification can make them less stressful**. It is not unlike being scared by a dark figure in a cloak and a horrific mask. Once the mask is removed and the light is on, you are usually not afraid of the figure at all.

4. Control

Not only is this the best way of reducing stress, **control of life is the reward for your efforts in unwinding and understanding life**. The majority of people can learn to unwind and understand life, but not everyone will be able to control life. The reason is that many individuals, deep down, do not want to have this power. Indeed they may be afraid of the responsibility. In reality, it is not possible to control more than about 75% of life so the power and responsibility is limited. However, it is a much stronger position to be in where 25% of your life is in turmoil (as opposed to 100%).

Perhaps **the greatest value of control is that it provides**

choice. You can choose how you spend your time, your solutions to problems and what sort of decisions you make. When one exercises choices with an awareness of stress, then stress becomes less important. It is like when you buy a young puppy, being aware of all the mischief (both intentional and unintentional) of such an animal, it is a lot easier for the puppy to become a member of the family. **Whenever you exercise choice, there is a greater tolerance of stress**. Having said this, young puppies are very stressful, even after you have chosen!!

BE BETTER

The object of life is to be better. If you can improve on what you started with, you have made progress. In the first quarter of life, very many individuals succeed in improving themselves. For some reason, this does not seem to continue throughout life, and most people quickly find themselves in positions where they cease to improve. Instead, more and more time is spent on trying to be happy. The paradox is that it is easy to be happy when one is improving oneself; it is very difficult to be happy if one's whole existence is directed at finding happiness.

1. Self-improvement

To improve yourself, **you need to develop skills**. Several important skills have been described in this book: skills of unwinding, understanding and controlling life. These skills are worth developing as they allow self-improvement. It is like being born with a packet of seeds. Somehow, sometime during your life, you will have to create the right growing conditions for these seeds. It will take time and effort. There will be many persuasive arguments why you should not spend time on growing seeds. Yet, you must, because you have been given them. You avoid facing the problem until it is almost too late. Then, you do what you should have done a long time ago. Eventually, you look upon the results of planting and nurturing your seeds – a cascade of colour. You stop, you think; and **you wonder why you had not done it before**.

Many are attracted to the characteristics of youth. To most, this means good health and an active life. Yet, these are not the best characteristics. **The best characteristics of youth are a willingness to learn and not being afraid of new situations**. If you can approach life as a youngster, with a drive to improve yourself, the active life and good health will follow. If you cannot, then it is a downhill journey from now on. Perhaps, this is a time to remember that the only difference between a rut and a grave is a matter of depth.

2. Happiness

Happiness is a direct result of being better. First, it should be said that "being better" is not the same as "being successful". Instead, "being better" is simply improving on what you started with – growing and nurturing seeds into plants. What is happiness? **The potential for happiness is the only way that all men and women are equal**. Much has been written about happiness, but there is still much misunderstanding about this condition.

Everyone has the same potential for happiness in any unit of time. Thus, the rich man and the poor man have the same potential for happiness. The poor man who has one day's holiday in a year could have as much happiness in that day as the rich man. The rich man has his happiness spread out over the year, whereas the poor man has it all in one day. Who would be a rich man?

The greatest shame about happiness is that **many people refuse to be happy.** For some reason perhaps because it is free, many feel that they can only be happy under certain conditions. Thus, if they are unemployed, ill, divorced or separated, there is a great reluctance to be happy. This is a great shame because these opportunities to be happy will not come again.

Regret of the past is also a great handicap to being happy. Yet, the lessons of the past are there so that one can learn for the future. The lesson is that happiness must be taken. It is quite difficult to understand why so many people are continually regretting yesterday's missed opportunities. Somehow, it is a vicious circle that can be impossible to break. It is hoped that this book will allow its readers to recognize these situations, and to have the skills to break these vicious circles.

To be better is both simple and difficult. It is simple in that you need to improve yourself and to be happy. It is difficult because there are many aspects of your past and present which are preventing you from doing these things. The skills of unwinding, understanding and controlling of life will enable you to overcome the past and the present. Simply, to be better is easy if you want it to be.

SUMMARY

1. Ill health due to stress may produce minor illness, serious illness or affect pre-existing illness.

2. Minor illnesses result in a large variety of complaints which affect every single system in the body. The symptoms come and go. Their presence is related to the extent of the stress.

3. Serious illnesses may develop when stress is present for a long time. Certain personalities may be more prone to serious illnesses.

4. In those with pre-existing illness, stress may make matters worse. The ultimate return to good health may be dependant on the removal or reduction of stress.

5. Stress may be reduced by behaviour, the abililty to unwind, understand and control life.

6. The use of exercise, food, smoking and drug misuse are common behavioural reactions to stress. The best way of reducing stress is to be able to unwind.

7. To understand yourself allows the recognition of stress and identification of problems. To control life is the great reward of being able to unwind. It allows you to exercise choice.

8. To be better one needs to attempt self-improvement (by developing new skills) and take your opportunities to be happy. Thus, the ability to be better is both simple and difficult.

CHAPTER NINE
YOUR LIFE

Colin was very pleased. His new doctor had succeeded in getting him to lose 2 stone in weight in one month, and all of his new summer clothes were fitting him perfectly. His friend, Ian, was reluctant to spend money, but amazed at Colin's progress and was determined to find the secret of Colin's success. One day, after Ian had bought Colin a large meal and lots of wine, Ian asked:

"How does your doctor get you to lose weight?"

"Oh, it's very easy. He has an evil-smelling liquid which I take before going to bed. As soon as I go to sleep, I seem to be on a tropical island where there are hundreds of beautiful women and I am the only man. These wonderful women chase me all night. By the morning when I wake up, I have lost a few pounds of fat. Yet, it was just wonderful!"

Ian was impressed and arranged to see Colin's doctor. He

duly received his bottle of medicine, and within a week Ian had lost a stone in weight.

"How are you finding the treatment?" his doctor asked him one week later.

"Its great. But I have one complaint," he replied.

"What is it?" asked his doctor.

"Well," said Ian, "my friend Colin has wonderful dreams of being chased by beautiful women. I have terrible dreams of being chased by a tribe of hungry cannibals who haven't ate for a week. Why can't I have dreams like Colin?"

"That's easy," replied the doctor. "Colin is a private patient. You are on the National Health Service so I have to treat you faster."

Your life is what you make of it. Many people will arrive at the same destination by different routes. Both Ian and Colin succeeded in losing a lot of weight. That, in itself, was quite an accomplishment. However, Ian was unhappy as Colin was achieving a similar result in a much more enjoyable way. Thus, **there are two important considerations in dealing with stress: the result and the way it was achieved**. Unfortunately, the way some results are achieved are very stressful.

The aim of this book is for you to choose a path that suits you. For some, the stressful path is right; for most, stress-free solutions would be more suitable. Hopefully, unwinding, understanding and controlling life will allow you to achieve a result that you want. If you can also choose the most enjoyable path for you, then, you deserve all that you achieve.

As stated in previous chapters, **stress is a process in which the resources of the person are matched against the demands of the environment**. In this chapter, ways of reducing stress will be considered in terms of reducing the demands of the environment or increasing a person's own resources.

DEMANDS OF THE ENVIRONMENT

The demands of the environment vary with the stage in your life. Nevertheless, the demands may be considered under three broad categories: your family and friends; your job and your financial situation. At different times each of these categories may be more or less important. However, none of these categories should be neglected for a long time.

1. Family and friends

Your family and friends can be the source of much happiness and enjoyment. Not surprisingly, family and friends are also the source of stress. The reason for these positive and negative emotions is that **you both receive and give support to family and friends**. At times of your own personal stress, you are very grateful for such support. Unfortunately, it is not uncommon for your family and friends to need your support at the same time that you need theirs. Such situations can be very difficult to resolve and many relationships have been terminated because of these problems. Paradoxically, a time when both partners of a relationship are under stress, is also a time when there is an opportunity of becoming closer. By providing mutual support and understanding even though the problems may be different, individuals may reach a high point in their relationship. It is similar to experiencing a common difficulty, such as a natural disaster, when great friendships can be made.

In everyone's life, there are **precious times**. These precious times are not only memorable, but also are usually at crucial times of an individual's life. Some of these times are common to all: important birthdays, the first job, holidays, marriage, birth of children, deaths, accidents and illnesses. Precious times may also be very individual, such as the long conversation with someone on the train or the unexpected generosity of a stranger. **The potential problem for the individual is that your family and friends expect your support during their precious times**. Fortunately, in the vast majority of cases, it is not difficult for you to provide support. The problem arises only when there are competing requests from different individuals for your time.

How do you know whom to support? If you are faced by an illness of a relative and an impending divorce of a friend, whom do you support? Most individuals would like to support both. However, if there is not enough time for both, what do you do? The answer depends on your priorities. But the simple rule is that the **family comes before friends**. And among your friends, you owe some more than others. Again, the simple rule is to **repay the friends whom you owe first**. However, these rules are only general and the individual circumstances of a situation needs to be considered.

2. Job

Many people are unhappy with their job. Often, jobs seem to choose individuals rather than individuals choosing jobs. Opportunities can occur at the right time and before you are aware of the consequences, you have been in the job several years. Thus, it becomes too difficult to change your job, and somehow your future has been decided for you. For many people, redundancy can be a blessing in disguise. **One's job can produce stress in three main ways: the working conditions, the people at work and the potential for self-improvement in the job.**

As one is working 8-9 hours per day, the working conditions are very important. Obviously, someone who likes working outdoors is less happy indoors, and may become suicidal working in a mine shaft. Similarly, if someone hates working at night, a night job is not ideal. While these examples may appear obvious, other factors in the working conditions are easily overlooked. Noise, bright lights, draughts, heat, cold, dirt, smells and a host of minor factors may cause considerable discomfort to a worker. These factors need to be identified as potentially stressful. However, **often workers do not realise that certain working conditions are stressful until they leave the job**.

More important than the working conditions are the people that one works with. This can be especially important if the staff is small as difficult individuals cannot be avoided. Your position relative to the other staff is also important. If you are the boss, you need to be confident in your managerial skills. If you are not, an aggressive employee could cause you more stress than you could give him/her. As with working conditions, it is important to identify your problems at work. When this is done, one can attempt to solve the problems (Chapter Seven, Control life). **The people at work are a big source of stress**.

Sadly, most people work to live. Working for money is not ideal. It would be better if you worked because you wanted to do the job, whether or not you were paid. In today's world, such an attitude is exceptionally rare. Most people would be content to be happy in their job. Happiness comes when there is self-improvement. As countless students could testify, training conditions in any craft or profession could be horrific; yet, **this stress in a job can be tolerated if there is self-improvement and an end in sight**.

A job is a measure of how you see yourself, and how others see you. Yet, your job is a large part of your life and a source of great stress. The results of stress are least when you like the working conditions, the people you work with and your job gives you the opportunity to improve yourself.

3. Finances

Today's world is materialistic and so one's income is a major concern. Indeed, many would regard the best reason for changing a job is an increase in salary. This is because most people do not understand finances and the use of money.

There is a great emphasis on an individual's income. Indeed, some individuals change jobs, work long hours and subject themselves to great stress with the sole objective of increasing their income. However, income is only one factor, and perhaps the least important.

Expenditure is the key to understanding finances. **It is more important to control what you spend than what you earn**. This simple truth can be seen by the wonderful achievements of many poor families. It also makes sense. It is easy to spend less than you earn; it is difficult to try and earn more than you can spend. The world's resources are limited and so one should not try to have everything.

Many find themselves in financial problems. Often this is because expenditure has not been controlled. For some reason, people usually feel that their finances will suddenly improve. **Most people do not make difficult financial decisions early enough**. With finances, it is best to over-react, and take decisions early rather than late. Perhaps, even more important is the use of money. **Money is a tool to reduce your stress and bring you happiness**. Yet, most people live their lives in a way in which they need more money, and there is a great stress to earn more. They then do not control expenditure and spend extravagantly on things which may make them happier. More usually, these things do not bring happiness. Rather than learn from the experience, these individuals conclude that if they had spent more, they would have been happier. The reality is that they are in love with the acquisition of money, and do not understand the uses of money.

PERSONAL RESOURCES

The personal resources of the individual allow the person to withstand the demands of the environment. **In trying to understand yourself, it is important to recognize your fears, weaknesses and strengths**. With this knowledge, you are able to judge your reactions to situations, and make right decisions.

1. Fears

Fears are very strong emotional reactions. Many people are easily forced into hurried decisions because of fears. **Many fears have their origin in childhood and early life**. Thus, if one's parents had tremendous financial problems, a child may grow up to be an adult with a great fear of financial insecurity. Such individuals may never make decisions in which there is a chance of them losing their jobs. Worse, they may force themselves to live with great stress at work because they are scared of financial insecurity.

Most people have general fears of the future. Many of these fears such as the destruction of the planet, pollution and global warming are shared by most of the population. For many, these fears are real, and in sharp contrast to their personal life where there is no fear of disaster. This allows people to make good general decisions such as in using unleaded petrol, but bad personal decisions such as in marriage. Thus, **good decisions may depend on some fear**, but this fear must not be overwhelming or a result of strong childhood emotions.

2. Strengths

Strengths are skills which have been developed, often in an area where someone is gifted. As some fear can help to make good decisions, **strengths can be a handicap**. Thus, for example, individuals who are strong at a particular sport may find themselves playing this sport throughout life. Often, their skills and enjoyment diminish with time. If they had been less gifted, they could have tried several sports and probably had more enjoyment from each.

Everyone should be aware of their strengths. Some skills are particularly easy to identify such as a good memory, aptitude for figures, or gifted at music. Unfortunately, such skills can also produce a lot of stress. Other skills are more difficult to identify such as someone who is content, happy to be alive or does not get angry quickly. Nevertheless, these latter skills are much more useful in dealing with stress. Thus, **some strengths produce stress, whereas other strengths are useful in dealing with stress**.

The ideal situation is where individuals are aware of how their strengths may influence their behaviour in any situation. Such knowledge comes from being able to observe your own behaviour. Hopefully, the Plan to unwind (Chapter Five) will allow you to obtain this information about yourself (Chapter Six, Understand life).

3. Weakness

Some people are more aware of their strengths, whereas others are more aware of their weaknesses. **Weaknesses are potential gaps in your ability to deal with stress**. The consequences are most severe in those individuals who are not able to see their own weaknesses. If you can identify your weaknesses, then it is possible to make decisions that will avoid these areas.

As more care is taken with areas of weaknesses, it is possible that these areas may become strengths. There are numerous stories of individuals who hated, and were hopeless at public speaking; yet, in time became accomplished speakers who were in great demand. This should not be surprising. With time and effort, it is possible to develop many skills. With a proper understanding of all problems, **it is possible to turn fears and weakness into strengths**. However, the greatest value of such conversions is that the process increases the individual's personal resources and reduces the amount of stress.

CHOOSING

The freedom to choose is a wonderful gift. Yet, many individuals who have this freedom refuse to choose. Instead, they are influenced by the demands of the environment and the limits of their personal resources. Thus, **many people**

have decisions made for them. They are usually unhappy with these decisions and frequently complain, however, they refuse to choose for themselves. What does choosing for yourself involve? It involves a recognition that other people's choices affect your health and personal objectives.

1. Health

If you try to be what someone else wants you to be, it is only a matter of time before you develop ill health. This is because if you are not yourself, it is a masquerade; and, it is only possible to masquerade for a short time. Thereafter, illnesses may follow (Chapter Eight, Be better). As it is your life, **if there is going to be ill health, it would be better if it is a result of your choosing** rather than the choosing of others. It is obvious. Yet, it is more common for people to allow others to choose, and then complain.

Illness is a good marker of your well-being. If you are under stress and unhappy, you should try and find why this is. **You are responsible for yourself and for your own health**. If illness is a result of the choosing of others, you have a simple choice: either continue to be ill, or be better by choosing for yourself. If illness is a result of your own choosing, your choices are far more difficult: you have to reduce the demands on yourself, or increase your personal resources.

2. Personal objectives

It is great to know what you want out of life. Most of the population are so busy living that they do not have time to consider what they want. Sadly, **it is just as important to know if you can get what you want out of life**. Many people feel that they can achieve anything. At best, this is untrue; at worse, this may result in your death. Whilst it is important for everyone to have objectives or dreams, it is also critical for you to be aware of a timescale for these objectives. Some are pretty unlikely such as winning the football pools or becoming a billionaire. Other objectives, such as learning to drive, learning a foreign language, completing a course or owning your own house have variable, reasonable timescales. **You need to know how reasonable your personal objectives are**. Then, you will be able to live your life within these timescales. It is also important to know if your personal objectives are needs or wants. As mentioned before (Chapter Seven, Control Life), this distinction is necessary before you can establish priorities. It is just not possible to have enough time to do all the things you would like. Therefore, you have to establish the things that you need to do, as opposed to those that you would want to do. Each individual should **establish those personal objectives which are needs and from these choose the most important**.

3. Reduce demands

Reducing the demands of the environment is similar to controlling your finances by reducing expenditure. Once you have established personal objectives, there will be a degree of stress. **If this stress results in ill health, you need to cope by reducing the demands on yourself.** The easiest first step is to reduce your social obligations. After these, you need to look at your commitments to family and friends. Some of these relationships are unequal with your putting into the relationships more than you are getting out of them. **Relationships are not unlike financial investments**: in bad relationships, you keep on giving with very little return.

Many feel that it is wrong to look upon relationships like financial investments. They would explain that people are different from money. All of this is true. It is obviously wrong to live your life in terms of a financial statement. The message in this book is that you should be aware of all that is happening to you. If you are aware of the situation, and choose to give more to the relationship, this is your choice. However, if all of your relationships are like this, you must not be surprised if you have difficulty in coping with life. Even with the best financial advice, some investments go wrong, but if they all go wrong, you will soon be bankrupt.

4. Increase resources

This is the most enjoyable aspect of coping with stress. Self-improvement as mentioned before (Chapter Eight: Be better), is an obligation. As the demands of the environment increase, increased personal resources can maintain the balance. **This book is aimed at increasing the individual's personal resources.**

Personal resources are not unlike a gift of money. Once you have been given the money, you still have the difficult decision of how to spend it. **Choosing how you use your personal resources is very difficult**. You should carefully consider the demands of your personal objectives on your health. Some objectives are very demanding and are equivalent to using up all of your money. Other objectives are able to make you richer. If the demands of the environment are great, you should not choose a path that would further diminish your personal resources. However, if the demands of the environment are small, then you have a golden opportunity to choose personal objectives that are very demanding.

The objective of life is to maintain a balance between the needs upon you and your resources. This book is aimed at making you aware of this balance. It also emphasises that you need to make choices. It is your life and if you can understand and control life, you will be better. If you cannot ill health, poverty and unhappiness are on the horizon.

SUMMARY

1. In your life, it is not only important to achieve certain results, but also it is important how these results were achieved.

2. The demands of the environment vary with your stage of life. Family and friends give support to you, but expect to receive support, especially during precious times.

3. A job is a great source of stress. The working conditions, the people at work and the potential for self-improvement determine the level of stress at work.

4. Personal finances are another great source of stress. It is more important to control what you spend than what you earn, and to make difficult financial decisions early.

5. In assessing your personal resources, it is important to recognize fears, strengths and weaknesses.

6. Many fears have their origin from childhood; but good decisions may depend on some fear. Everyone should be aware of their strengths, but strengths can produce stress. It is possible to turn fears and weaknesses into strengths.

7. You should not be afraid of choosing. You are responsible for your health and for choosing the way you want to live.

8. You should identify your personal objectives and know how reasonable or necessary they are.

9. If you are under stress, you need to reduce the demands of the environment or increase your personal resources.

CHAPTER TEN
THE GAME OF LIVING

The young university student was quite proud of his intellectual capabilities, and took every opportunity to demonstrate his knowledge to the old aged pensioner on the train. The pensioner was indeed impressed by the student's knowledge and he was frequently nodding his head in amazement. Eventually the student said to the pensioner:

"Do you know what is the reason I have so much knowledge?"

"No," replied the pensioner.

"Well," continued the student, "it is to make money. For example, you ask me a question and if I do not know the answer I shall pay you five pounds. Then, I shall ask you a question and if you do not know the answer, you will pay me five pounds."

"No! No!" replied the pensioner. "You are much better educated than I. You can give me five pounds, but I shall give you only one pound."

The student thought for a second, but he was feeling generous and agreed to the new conditions. He also gestured to the pensioner to ask his question.

"Okay." said the pensioner, "What has four legs in the water, three legs on land and two legs in the air?"

The student's mouth opened and he gasped. Several hours later he agreed that he did not know the answer, and paid the pensioner five pounds.

"What is the answer?" asked the student.

"Oh," replied the pensioner, "I do not know either. Here is your one pound."

The use of knowledge to make money has always been a dangerous business which can run into trouble. Similarly, it is easy to ask questions to which there are no answers. The essence of this book is that the Plan to unwind and the results of unwinding will allow the reader to ask questions, and find the answers.

This chapter has been called "The Game of Living". Many would say that life is far too serious to be called a game. Although this is in general correct, many professional sportspeople have serious approaches to games. Indeed, **to do well in a game you have to be very serious**. A game is also an event that is observed. Again, to do well in life, you must be able to see yourself the way that others see you. This chapter considers the Game of living in terms of skills, disasters, losing, winning and how you can be better at this important game.

SKILLS

Every game requires the individual to spend time and effort at developing certain skills for that game. This could range from learning peculiar words for the game of scrabble to a whole way of life that involves every hour of the day such as in Sumo wrestling. Within these extremes, **many individuals spend many hours every week developing skills in various sporting games,** such as golf, cricket or football. This time is not regarded as work but as enjoyment. Indeed, a lot of people would take a whole week's holiday from work to develop game skills.

The skills that are needed for the Game of living are: the ability to unwind (Chapter Five); an understanding of your life (Chapter Six); and control of your life (Chapter Seven). It will take great time and effort to acquire these skills. As with all games, you will also need to be serious and committed. Like other games, the best results are obtained if you want to become adept, and you take every opportunity to practice your skills. If you look for every opportunity and excuse to avoid unwinding you are destined to be unskilled. **The amateur feels good with one unwinding session a week; the professional feels guilty with two unwinding sessions a**

day. To be better, you must also see success from your efforts in your life. If the results are not good, something is wrong; you need to re-read the earlier chapters in this book.

There are always very many good reasons for not having an unwinding session. The usual ones are: you have had a hard day; you are not up to it; the house has to be cleaned; there is the washing or ironing to do; or, you have to talk to the husband/a relative/the cat/the plant. **All of these excuses would not suffer if you delayed them for half an hour**. Indeed, after an unwinding session you could be better, and so a small delay could be good for all concerned.

The best attitude is one in which you looked upon an unwinding session as if you had bought a new gramophone record of your favourite singer. You would be taking every opportunity to play it. You would be saying: .

"It would only take a minute."

"I need a break."

"It would put me in a better mood."

"It will make me feel better."

If one said these things about an unwinding session, success would be assured. However, you must not only say it, but you must also mean it.

DISASTERS

Why are some people great in disasters, and others are totally unprepared for disasters? Some understanding of these questions can be gained from **looking at yourself as a submarine of life**. For many people, their entire lives are spent in port so that the submarine does not face adverse weather conditions. For others, any time out of port is spent on the surface so all the resources are not fully tested. Those who are good in disasters, have a life in which their submarine is frequently submerged. Worse, the submarine is able to withstand mines and depth charges. With this analogy, the mines and depth charges, are the demands of the environment (family, friends, job and finances). **You can only become good in disasters by having practice in dealing with such situations**.

It is also useful to think of the demands of the environment as separate compartments in the submarine. Thus, for example your family would be one compartment and your friends would be in another compartment. All of these compartments communicate with each other. However, the doors can be locked so that each compartment is separate. Sadly, some individuals only have one compartment to their lives, and this is usually their job. If there is a disaster such as being made unemployed, it is similar to a depth charge or mine exploding in this compartment. For individuals with only one compartment in their lives, the submarine would sink. Therefore, **for living you should have more than one compartment in your life**.

124

Lucky individuals have several compartments to their lives. Again, the test is what happens in a disaster. If there is an explosion in one compartment, the submarine would not sink if this compartment can be locked off from the other compartments. Therefore, the doors need to be watertight. Doors are only watertight if they have been correctly maintained. Thus, for dealing with disasters, **you need to spend time and effort in maintaining all of the compartments in your life**. This means that you should not spend too much time in one compartment to the detriment of others.

LOSING

In the Game of living, there is little reward for the losers. As life becomes more stressful and competitive, the numbers who are homeless or jobless will increase. In many ways, it is becoming more and more important to be able to control your life. Problems usually arise out of poor control. This book is aimed at showing the value of unwinding (Chapter Five); the wisdom of understanding your life (Chapter Six); and the usefulness of controlling your life (Chapter Seven). **Losing the Game of living is associated with poor control of your life**. Poor control is usually a result of an unproductive use of time, little understanding of the reward/effort ratio, and bad decisions.

Although many would like to separate their job from their recreational games, similar rules apply to both. Thus, if you are good at either, you enjoy them more and the chances of your losing are less. Yet, there are important differences. After losing a game of tennis, golf or football, as a result of bad decisions you can console yourself by saying "Playing the game is more important than winning. I enjoyed the exercise and I met my friends". With a recreational game, activity and social interactions are rewards for bad decisions. **In the Game of living, ill health is the reward of bad decision**.

Like sporting games, everyone is in a type of league or list. The more bad decisions you make, the lower you will be in the list. In recreational games, the person who is the worse player may be quite popular, especially if the person is hopeless but is a good loser. Everyone loves a good loser and it can be wonderful playing a game with someone who cannot win. In the Game of living, such popularity is a luxury. It is like the poor paying for the life style of the rich. One would not choose to do it. Yet, **many individuals in wanting to be popular, suffer in order to allow others to benefit**. If this is a free choice, it is a tremendous gift. Unfortunately, in most cases the individuals who suffer are unaware of what is happening.

The great sadness about being on a losing ticket is that things usually get worse. Common solutions to this situation are excessive alcohol consumption or drug misuse. The downward spiral continues relentlessly. However, **losing can always be stopped; it requires the strength and the will to control life**. The will to live is not the same as the will to exist. The will to live is about winning the Game of living.

126

WINNING

Many believe that winning is the only important result. If one cheats, lies or degrades oneself, it does not matter; nothing matters as long as one wins. This may be true for a few in some recreational games. It is totally untrue in the Game of living. In **the Game of living, winning is personal and individual**. Spectators, judges and umpires are irrelevant; even opponents are totally unnecessary. The reason is that in the Game of living, you are all of these things. Thus, if you cheat, you cheat yourself; if you lie, you lie to yourself.

The **object of the Game of living is for you to be better**. This is measured in your self-improvement and happiness (Chapter Eight, Be better). These measurements are personal and do not relate to anyone else. Thus, if in your life, you improve from one unit to one thousand units, you have done as well as someone who improves from one thousand to a million units. The millionaire would have a lot more physical attributes, but you could be as happy.

At an early stage, you must accept that all are not equal. This is one of the worst lies that is told to children. It is painfully obvious that the world is full of people with unequal amounts of money, skills, abilities and intellect. We all start from different points. Thus, what is important is what we make out of the Game of living. The only way that the world makes sense is if the **measurements of individual success are self-improvement and happiness**. These measurements are individual and personal. They reflect your ability to improve yourself from your own, individual starting position. The object of this book is to allow you to do this.

Hopefully, you will also enjoy playing the Game of living. If you develop the skills for living, you will be better. Most people become happier when they have the skills to play the game better. If you have read all of this book, you will know that happiness is there for you to take. Do not be afraid of taking happiness as it will not be there forever.

SUMMARY

1. To do well in the Game of living you have to be serious. You need to develop skills (unwinding, understanding and controlling life). You should not make excuses to avoid unwinding sessions.

2. People who are good in the disasters of life have had practice in dealing with such situations.

3. Your life is like a submarine. You should have more than one compartment to your submarine, and you should maintain all of the compartments in your submarine.

4. Losing the Game of living is common, and associated with poor control of life. Poor control is usually a result of an

unproductive use of time, little understanding of the reward/effort ratio and bad decisions.

5. In the Game of living, ill health is the reward of bad decisions. Many individuals in wanting to be popular suffer in order to allow others to benefit. Losing the Game of living can always be stopped, but it requires the strength and the will to control life.

6. In the Game of living, winning is personal and individual. The object of the game is for you to get better. The measurements of such success are self-improvement and happiness.

CHAPTER ELEVEN
CONCLUSION

I have observed many patients who are suffering the **ill-effects of living** in a modern society. Their predicament was a result of their lack of skills in dealing with modern life. It was **not their fault**. Indeed, many patients are totally unaware of why they have ended up with ill health. It all seems to be a cruel twist of fate.

Ill health usually results when the demands of the environment (family, friends, job and finances) are greater than the resources of the individual. This book advocates a Plan to unwind (Chapter Five). The word **"unwind"** has been chosen rather than "relaxation" because this book emphasizes mental as well as physical relaxation. This book is also about "undoing", "unravelling" and "disentangling" **life's problems**.

A great benefit of being able to unwind is that you will be able to see yourself in the Game of living (Chapter Ten). If you can be objective about yourself, you will be able to obtain information about yourself. Information is critical in being able to **understand your life** (Chapter Six), especially as it allows you to identify problems. The proper identification of problems is an **advanced phase of mind control** (Chapter Five).

As one becomes better at unwinding, there can be progress to the **control of life**. This involves good use of time, an awareness of the reward/effort ratio and decision-making (Chapter Seven). These skills also allow you to solve the problems of life, and make **good decisions**.

With life's stresses, many patients develop **minor illness** (Chapter Eight). This can mean that there are complaints in every system of the body. Worse, minor illness may become **serious**; and those with **pre-existing illness may deteriorate**. In these situations, the Plan to unwind (Chapter Five) offers a solution. However, to be better, you need to attempt self-improvement (by developing new skills), and also to take your opportunities to be happy.

This book enables you to see your life in terms of **demands** being made on you and your **personal resources**. It attempts to encourage you to identify your personal objectives. With this information, it is possible for you to reduce the demands being made on you, and to increase your personal resources (Chapter Nine). Lastly, the **Game of living** is explained (Chapter Ten). It is emphasized that the object of this Game is individual and personal. The measurement of success is self-improvement and happiness.

It is hoped that this book will not only be used by ill people, but also by those who would like to develop **skills for living**. Prevention of illness is far superior to the cure of ill health. To live in the West is not easy. Every day, there are tremendous demands on the individual. These demands may become overwhelming. When this happens, ill health may result. This need not happen. The Game of living (Chapter Ten) can be won. This book provides the tools for all, both ill and well. You can use these tools to build whatever life you would like. You will need to have commitment. You will need to devote time and effort. You could have **self-improvement and happiness**.

APPENDIX: EMBME

The plan to unwind (Chapter Five) consists of five stages: Entrance, Muscles, Breathing, Mind and Exit. The stages can easily be remembered by the palindrome, **EMBME**.

Many individuals have been concerned on how this word should be pronounced. Some are happiest with three separate words: em-be-me. Others are more comfortable with two words: emb-me. One individual has even managed to produce one almost continuous sound for embme; it was not dissimilar to the famous mantra "OM". The truth is that it does not matter. Each individual may pronounce embme in whatever way that he/she feels most comfortable.

The famous "Jesus Prayer" in which the word "Jesus" is repeated like a mantra can be instructive. It is quite surprising how many ways it is possible to pronounce the word "Jesus". Yet, there can be no one right pronounciation. A mantra should be individual to each person.

BETTER RECOVERY FROM VIRAL ILLNESSES

(ISBN: 0 9511090 1 4)

by Dr Darrel Ho-Yen

The first edition was the first book published on Post Viral Fatigue Syndrome (myalgic encephalomyelitis, Royal Free Disease, Chronic Fatigue Syndrome).

The second edition of this popular book has been extensively rewritten with 14 chapters in 131 pages.

There are chapters on: terminology, case histories, diagnosis, symptoms, history, psychological problems, exercise, food allergies, self-help groups, employment, treatment, alternative medicine, outlook and a conclusion.

There have been many favourable comments by patients on this book, including "inspirational", "good sense", "practical advice", "the best".

Obtainable from: DODONA BOOKS

ISBN 0-951 11090-0-2-2

Publishers and distributors:
Dodona Books,
The Old Schoolhouse,
Kirkhill,
Inverness,
IV5 7PE.